Library and Archives Canada Cataloguing Publication

Canadian Firearms Safety Course Modules: Student Handbook, 5th edition

Also available in French under the title: Cours canadien de sécurité dans le maniement des armes à feu, manuel de l'étudiant.

(Également disponible en français sous le titre, Cours canadien de sécurité dans le maniement des armes à feu, manuel de l'étudiant, 5ᵉ édition.)

ISBN 978-0-660-19947-4

Catalogue no.: PS99-2/1-1-2014E

Firearms--Canada--Safety measures.

Firearms ownership--Canada.

Firearms--Safety measures.

Gun control--Canada.

Royal Canadian Mounted Police (RCMP) / Canadian Firearms Program (CFP)

TS532.2.C36 2010 363.330971

This edition of the Canadian Firearms Safety Course Modules is produced by:

RCMP Headquarters
Ottawa ON K1A 0R2
Canada

Fax: 613-825-0297

PREFACE

Acknowledgements

Many organizations with an ongoing interest in firearm safety volunteered their time to review and comment on this Handbook during its review stages. The efforts and assistance of the many people involved (see below) are acknowledged and appreciated. Without their help and that of the following persons, this Handbook would not have been correctly reviewed:

- Chief Firearms Officers (CFOs) and their Staff

- Baldwin, Chris; Manager Conservation Services, Stewardship and Education Section Wildlife Division, Newfoundland & Labrador

- Batten, Shelly; Operations Manager, Firearms Safety Education Service of Ontario (FSESO), Ontario

- Cooper, A.C. (Tony); Firearms Safety Education Service of Ontario (FSESO), Ontario

- Halvorson, Tony; CFSC & CRFSC Master Instructor, Prince Edward Island

- Jones, Don; Chief Instructor, Retired, Firearms Safety Education Service of Ontario (FSESO), Ontario

- Martin, Allan; President, Instructors of Firearms Safety Association (IOFSA) of British Columbia, CFSC & CRFSC Master Instructor, British Columbia

- Sadauskas, Sherrie (McAdam); Firearms Officer, Halton Regional Police Service, Chief Instructor, Firearms Safety Education Service of Ontario (FSESO)

- Valiquette, Jean; Master Instructor for the Fédération québécoise des chasseurs et pêcheurs, Sécurité nature, for the province of Québec

Most importantly, the Royal Canadian Mounted Police (RCMP) / Canadian Firearms Program (CFP) wishes to acknowledge the talent and expertise of the certified Instructors of the Canadian Firearms Safety Course (CFSC) from across Canada, many of whom took the time and effort to provide written recommendations and suggestions in the development of this material.

Disclaimer

The improper use of firearms may result in serious injury. The material presented in this Handbook is intended to demonstrate the operation of firearms in accordance with safe handling techniques and an awareness of manufacturers' specifications and safety features.

The RCMP/CFP makes no warranties whatsoever, either express or implied, oral or written, in fact or by operation of law or otherwise, regarding the safety of any firearm or the use of any safety mechanism shown in the Handbook.

Individuals should use firearms in accordance with manufacturers' specifications and contact individual manufacturers as each model features different safety mechanisms and some of the techniques demonstrated might not be appropriate for certain firearms.

Ultimately, responsibility for firearm safety rests with the individual.

TABLE OF CONTENTS

TABLE OF CONTENTS

List of Figures

List of Tables

INTRODUCTION TO THE
CANADIAN FIREARMS SAFETY COURSE

INTRODUCTION TO THE CANADIAN FIREARMS SAFETY COURSE

Overview

The Canadian Firearms Safety Course (CFSC) is designed to apply to the broadest possible spectrum of novice firearm users. Existing firearm safety courses across Canada have a proven track record in the reduction of firearm-related incidents. However, most of these courses have been designed and delivered for firearms use in a specific activity. The CFSC is an introductory firearm safety course intended for all new firearm users.

Individuals who wish to acquire restricted firearms must also pass the Canadian Restricted Firearms Safety Course (CRFSC) tests.

The Canadian Firearms Program

The Canadian Firearms Program (CFP) is administered by the RCMP/CFP, which works with provincial CFOs and many community partners across the country in implementing the *Firearms Act* and its Regulations, and other related legislation regarding firearms.

The goal of the CFP is the safe and responsible use of firearms, and it includes a range of activities directed toward achieving that goal such as the following:

- the **licensing** of all firearm owners and businesses;
- the delivery of the **CFSCs**;
- **public education** regarding safe storage, transport and use of firearms; and
- **import and export controls**.

Licensing, registration and other Program information are recorded in the Canadian Firearms Information System, a national database that is managed by the RCMP/CFP. Certain information is available to law enforcement agencies to help them prevent and investigate firearms incidents and crime, consistent with the public safety objectives of the *Firearms Act*.

Your personal information is carefully protected by the CFP, consistent with the *Firearms Act* and its Regulations, federal and provincial privacy laws and other applicable statutes.

If you have any questions about the CFP, please contact us at the following location:

Canadian Firearms Program	
Telephone:	1-800-731-4000
Fax:	613-825-0297
E-mail:	cfp-pcaf@rcmp-grc.gc.ca
Address:	Royal Canadian Mounted Police / Canadian Firearms Program Ottawa ON K1A OR2

You can also consult the *Firearms Act* and its Regulations directly via the RCMP/CFP website.

The RCMP/CFP wishes you the best in following the CFSC for the class(es) of firearm you wish to acquire and/or possess. Please note that all CFSC instructors and examiners must be designated by the CFO for the province or territory in which you are taking the course.

Course Objectives

Firearm owners have social responsibilities. By completing this course, you will be instructed on what these responsibilities are. You will learn how to do the following:

- handle firearms and ammunition safely;

- use firearms and ammunition safely;

- comply with firearms laws;

- store non-restricted firearms and ammunition safely;

- display non-restricted firearms and ammunition safely; and

- transport non-restricted firearms and ammunition safely.

The CFSC consists of two parts. One is classroom instruction. The other is learning the material in this Handbook. There will be both written and practical examinations. Successfully passing them will demonstrate the knowledge and skills you have gained in the course. Live firing exercises, however, are not offered as part of this course.

During the course, some topics are discussed and explored several times. This will help you learn and retain the content. Leaving anything out of the course will reduce the amount you learn. This applies to all assignments, exercises or examinations given by your instructor.

The course emphasizes safe storage, display, transportation, handling and use of non-restricted firearms, but safety depends on more than just safe physical actions.

Safe handling must include greater knowledge of the firearms themselves, ammunition, and the laws and regulations related to them.

Course Handbook

Safety also relies on your attitude about responsible handling and use of firearms. Pay close attention to the section on legal, ethical and social responsibilities. Your safety and that of the people around you depends on it.

This book is an essential part of the course. The other parts are the classroom lessons and practical exercises given by the instructor. Together, they will help you learn how to safely handle firearms.

This book contains the following elements:

- the **Vital Four ACTS** of firearm safety;

- a brief history of firearms;

- information on firearms and ammunition and how they work;

- instructions on how to pick up, handle and carry non-restricted firearms safely;

- descriptions of how to unload, load and fire non-restricted firearms safely;

- descriptions of firing positions;

- instructions on range safety;

- instructions on the care and cleaning of non-restricted firearms;

- examples of factors leading to firearm incidents and the misuse of firearms;

- a summary of ethics and laws affecting firearm owners and users;

- information on how to store, display, transport and handle non-restricted firearms safely;

- a glossary of firearm terms; and

- appendices.

This is an introductory course. More information and training are available on the various shooting sports from their own qualified instructors, associations and local clubs. We recommend you contact them directly for further details.

Do not hesitate to contact provincial/territorial or local authorities for more detailed information on firearms laws and regulations in your area.

Consult the *Firearms Act* and its Regulations or a firearms officer, for information on controls affecting firearm and ammunition manufacturers, dealers and museum operators.

The Vital Four ACTS of Firearm Safety

Your instructor will refer to many different safety rules and guidelines. Time and again, the instructor will return to four basic rules. Any time you hear of an incident occurring, you can be sure at least one of these rules has been broken. These rules are known as the **Vital Four ACTS**.

The first letter of each rule becomes a letter in the acronym **ACTS**. You may want to think of these rules as acts you must carry out.

The Vital Four ACTS of Firearm Safety	
	Assume every firearm is loaded. • Regard any firearm as a potential danger.
	Control the muzzle direction at all times. • Identify the safest available muzzle direction. • Keep the firearm pointed in the safest available direction. • The muzzle of a firearm should not be pointed towards yourself or any other person.
	Trigger finger must be kept off the trigger and out of the trigger guard. • Do **NOT** put your finger on the trigger or inside the trigger guard when you pick up a firearm.
	See that the firearm is unloaded—PROVE it safe. • Do not handle the firearm unless you can properly **PROVE it safe**. • Check to see that both chamber and magazine are empty. Do this every time you handle a firearm, for any reason. • Pass or accept only open and unloaded firearms. It is an essential rule to adopt.

PROVE it safe Pointers

	PROVE it safe
☞	**P**oint the firearm in the safest available direction.
☞	**R**emove all ammunition.
☞	**O**bserve the chamber(s).
☞	**V**erify the feeding path.
☞	**E**xamine the bore for obstructions (visually or with a rod).

The firearm is now unloaded and safe until it leaves the direct control of the person who unloaded and PROVEd it safe.

Legal Responsibilities

As a firearm owner and user, you have legal as well as social responsibilities. These responsibilities are laid out in federal, provincial/territorial and municipal laws and regulations. The table below describes a few of the regulations that come from each level of government.

Table 1. Some Legal Responsibilities of Firearm Owners/Users

Government Level	Example of Law or Regulation
Federal (e.g., *Firearms Act* and its Regulations, *Criminal Code*)	• All firearm owners need a valid firearms licence. • If you are the holder of a valid firearms licence, you must inform the RCMP/CFP within 30 days after you change your address. • Persons holding a valid Possession and Acquisition Licence (PAL) may borrow, buy, inherit or otherwise acquire the same class of firearm that he/she is licensed to own.
Provincial/Territorial (e.g., *Game, Fish and Wildlife Acts*)	• Some provinces/territories may require anyone who hunts with a non-restricted firearm to wear blaze orange clothing. • Some restrict shooting across or within a certain distance of roads or dwellings. • Some provincial/territorial laws may limit your use of motorized vehicles while hunting or shooting.
Municipal/County/Local (e.g., Noise, Nuisance, Zoning, By-laws)	• Some municipalities or counties may not allow the discharge of a firearm under any circumstances within their boundaries. • Some will regulate firing times and/or closeness to dwellings.

Other Duties of Firearm Owners/Users

a. A firearm owner/user must also keep informed about the laws and regulations affecting the use of firearms and ammunition.

b. Going beyond what the regulations require will increase your safety. Some suggestions are listed below:

- Keep an inventory of your firearms. Also keep any supporting documents such as photographs and owner's manuals. Store these documents in a safe place. This will help you describe any firearm that may be stolen or lost. It will also be easier for you to find your owner's manual and records of service or repair.

- Keep informed. Changes may occur in laws and regulations from time to time. This can happen whether at the federal, provincial/territorial or municipal level.

- Avoid advertising about the firearms in your home. You may be inviting theft.

 Every person commits an offence who, without lawful excuse, points a firearm at another person, whether the firearm is loaded or unloaded, and is:

1. **guilty of an indictable offence and liable to imprisonment for a term not exceeding five years; or**
2. **guilty of an offence punishable on summary conviction (a fine of $5,000 and/or six months imprisonment).**

Reference: Subsections 87(1) and (2) of Part III of the *Criminal Code*

They may also lose their firearm, lose their licence, receive a fine, receive jail time and/or be prohibited from possessing a firearm for a period of time.

⚠ Every person who stores, displays, transports or handles any firearm in a manner contrary to the *Storage, Display, Transportation and Handling of Firearms by Individuals Regulations* is:

1. **guilty of an indictable offence and liable to imprisonment;**

   - in the case of a first offence, for a term not exceeding two years; and
   - in the case of a second or subsequent offence, for a term not exceeding five years; or

2. **guilty of an offence punishable on summary conviction (a fine of $5,000 and/or six months imprisonment).**

Reference: Subsections 86(2) and (3) of Part III of the *Criminal Code*

Not all firearms laws are included in this Handbook. If you have any doubts about the regulations, or if you need more information, contact the following:

- The RCMP website: http://www.rcmp-grc.gc.ca/cfp-pcaf
- CFP at 1-800-731-4000

MODULE 1:

INTRODUCTION TO FIREARMS

MODULE 1: INTRODUCTION TO FIREARMS

1.1. The evolution of firearms

1.1.0. Overview

By all accounts and historical references, it is believed that the Chinese were the first to develop explosive powder. They used it in fireworks and rockets. It was also invented at about the same time by the English alchemist Roger Bacon (1214-1292).

1.1.1. Cannon

a. People in the Middle Ages quickly learned to use black powder to launch balls or projectiles from a cannon. They did this by igniting the powder behind the ball or projectile in a cannon (Figure 1).

b. The burning powder in the cannon produced rapidly expanding gas which forced the ball or projectile out of the open end of the barrel.

c. Today, black powder and substitutes are used in different types of firearms and for various purposes (e.g., hunting, target shooting).

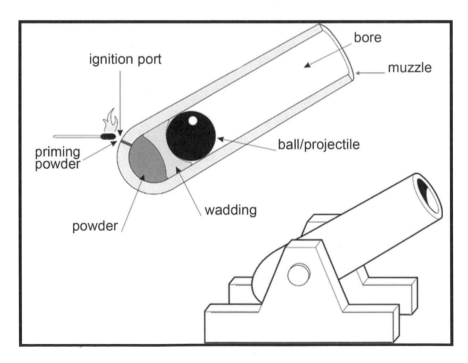

Figure 1. Cannon

1.1.2. Matchlocks

One of the earliest carried firearms was the matchlock (Figure 2). It was invented in the early 1400s. The matchlock made it possible for the user to aim and fire while holding the firearm with both hands, but rain or wind could put out the match/wick. In addition, the presence of incandescent particles near the powder could cause an incident.

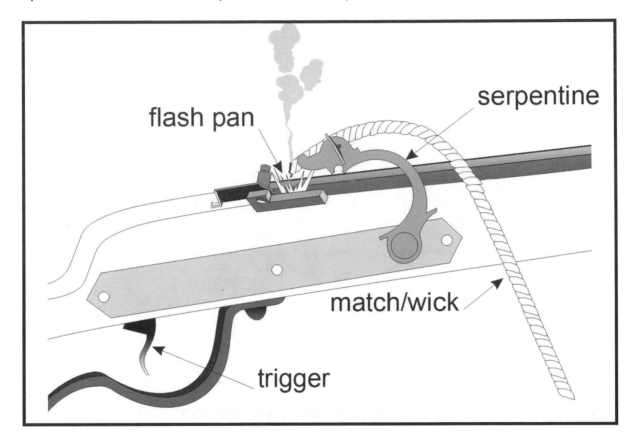

Figure 2. Matchlock Mechanism

1.1.3. Wheel locks

Two improved firing systems were developed in the 1600s. These were the wheel lock (Figure 3) and the flintlock (Figure 4). The wheel lock worked much like a modern cigarette lighter. The spring was wound up with a key. The wheel lock mechanisms were complex and expensive to make. Also, winding was slow and the spring often failed.

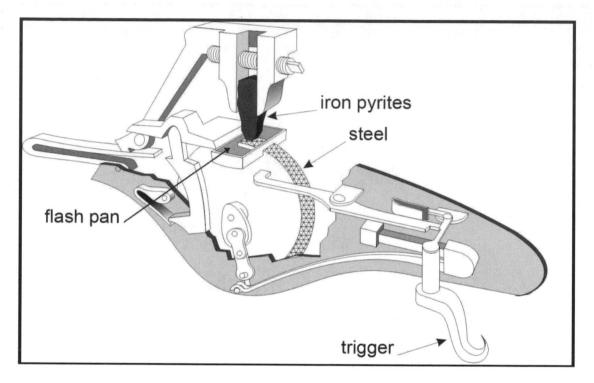

Figure 3. Wheel Lock Mechanism

1.1.4. Flintlocks

1. The flintlock (Figure 4) has an ignition mechanism similar to the wheel lock. It produced its spark by striking a flint against steel. Since it weighed less and was simpler and cheaper to make, it soon became more popular.

2. For centuries, flintlocks were the standard firearms (Figure 5). During this time, many improvements were introduced. One such improvement of the flintlock over the matchlock and wheel lock was the development of a more reliable ignition system.

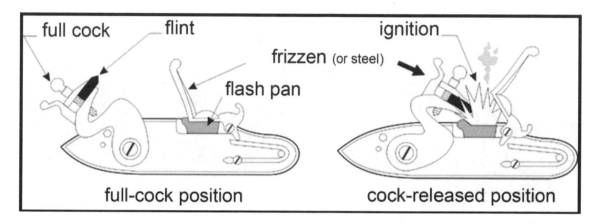

Figure 4. Flintlock Mechanism

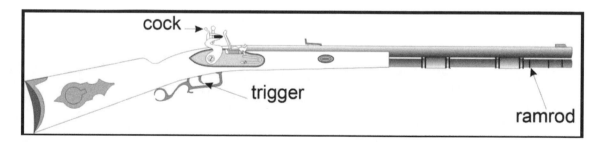

Figure 5. Flintlock Rifle

1.1.5. Percussion caps

The percussion cap (Figure 6) was developed in the early 1800s. It was a small metal case (cap) containing material that would explode when struck.

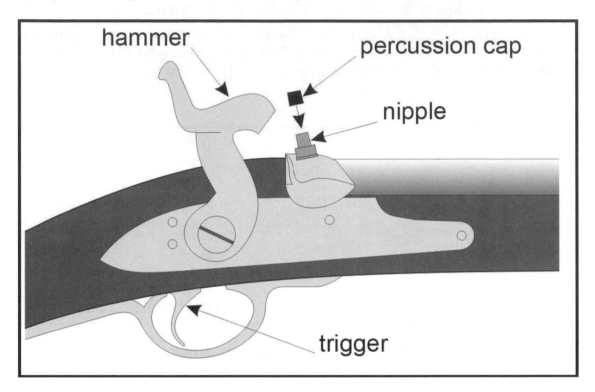

Figure 6. Percussion Cap

1.1.6. Evolution of Firearms

Table 2. Evolution of Firearms

Type (introduced)	Details ♦ Ignition System	Disadvantages
Matchlock (1400s)	<ul><li>first hand-held muzzleloader</li></ul> ♦ <ul><li>used a serpentine mechanism to plunge burning wick into the flash pan</li></ul>	<ul><li>failed in wind and rain</li></ul>
Wheel lock (1600s)	<ul><li>second hand-held muzzleloader</li></ul> ♦ <ul><li>operates like a modern cigarette lighter</li></ul>	<ul><li>mechanisms are complex and expensive to make</li><li>winding is slow and springs often fail</li></ul>
Flintlock (1600s)	<ul><li>same as wheel lock</li></ul> ♦ <ul><li>produced a spark by striking a flint against steel</li></ul> ♦ <ul><li>a more reliable ignition system</li></ul>	<ul><li>flints wear out or break</li><li>springs can fail</li></ul>
Percussion cap (1800s)	<ul><li>first step of the evolution to first repeating firearms</li></ul> ♦ <ul><li>a small metal case (cap) containing material that will explode when struck</li></ul>	<ul><li>cap separates from powder and bullet</li></ul>

1.1.7. Cartridges

a. All early firearms were muzzleloaders. They loaded through the muzzle. But muzzleloaders were slow to reload. They were also limited to one shot per barrel.

b. Attempts were made to develop firearms that loaded from the back. They were called breechloaders. However, these early attempts failed because the expanding gases from the burning powder charge leaked back through the breech parts.

c. In the mid-1800s, various cartridge types were developed that made breech loading practical. Eventually, metal-cased cartridges similar to modern ones were created (Figure 7).

d. These cartridges contained the bullet or shot, the main powder charge and the primer, in one package. Pulling the firearm trigger caused the firing pin to strike the primer. The flash from the primer ignited the powder charge. The burning charge caused the cartridge casing to expand. This sealed the breech to prevent gas leakage. The expanding gas launched the projectile down the barrel.

e. Cartridges had at least four advantages:

   1. They were easily loaded into the breech.

   2. The expanding case prevented gas leakage.

   3. They were largely weatherproof.

   4. They were more reliable.

f. Cartridges called shells were developed for use in shotguns. These too contain one or more projectiles, powder and primer in one container. In addition, a wad separates the powder from the projectiles. The cartridge casing may be made from metals or other materials such as paper or plastic.

g. Metallic cartridges and shotgun shells were easy to manufacture. Loading firearms also became simpler. This made repeating firearms practical.

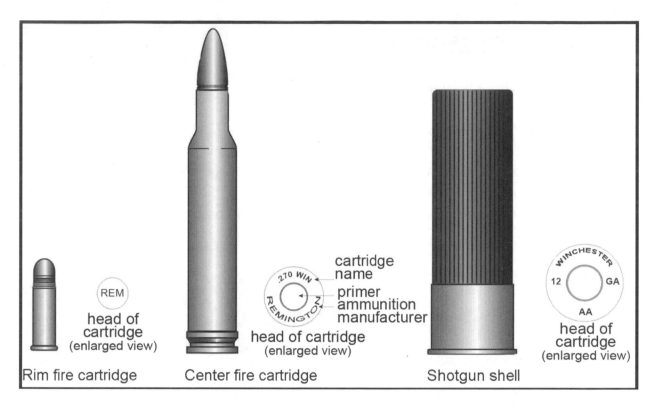

Figure 7. Examples of Modern Ammunition and Cartridge Head Stamps

1.2. Firearms in Canada

Since the 1500s, firearms have played a role in the history and development of Canada. They greatly expanded the range and effectiveness for hunting. People were willing to trade large quantities of furs for firearms and ammunition. Hunting provided a major source of food. It was often critical for survival, especially in poor crop years.

Later, the need for hunting to provide food became less necessary for most people for survival. However, many people today still rely on hunting as an important part of their lives.

Many have also turned to target shooting. Today, numerous shooting clubs and associations exist. Their members shoot various types of shotguns or rifles. A wide range of targets from clay to paper also exists.

There are also many gun collectors.

1.3. Review questions

1. List one of the advantages of modern cartridges.

2. What was the role of firearms in the development of Canada?

3. What is the role of the percussion cap in the firing sequence?

4. What is the name of the similar mechanism used in both the flintlock and the wheel lock?

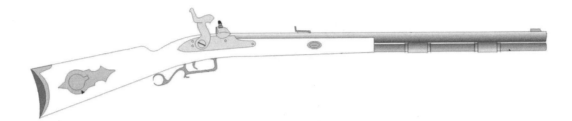

MODULE 2:

MUZZLELOADERS

MODULE 2: MUZZLELOADERS

2.1. Types of black powder

Table 3. Types of Black Powder

Fg	Very coarse granules of powder. Used in larger bore muskets.
FFg	Finer granules than the Fg. Used in muzzleloading shotguns, big-bore rifles and single-shot pistols of .45 calibre and up.
FFFg	Finer granules than the FFg and the most common type. Used in nearly all cap and ball revolvers.
FFFFg	The finest granules, also called priming powder. Used only in priming pans. **Never use this type of powder as powder charge.**

 Because of advancements in technology, some firearms are manufactured to handle either smokeless, black powder or black powder substitutes. It is emphasized that all individuals follow the manufacturer's instructions regarding powder types and safe loads. Please contact your local Black Powder Association for further information.

2.2. Muzzleloading firearms

2.2.0. Overview

a. Muzzleloading muskets, rifles and shotguns are still in use today. However, most modern muzzleloaders are reproductions of older designs (Figure 8).

b. This type of firearm is loaded through the muzzle. A measured amount of powder is poured through the muzzle into the barrel, followed by a patch and ball, bullet or shot. A hole located at the rear of the barrel just above the trigger allows a flash or spark to enter the barrel through the priming port and ignite the powder, firing the charge.

c. With flintlock muzzleloaders, the igniting spark is the result of the flint, held by the cock, hitting the frizzen. On percussion muzzleloaders, the flash is produced by the hammer striking a percussion cap.

d. Muzzleloading firearms use black powder or black powder substitutes. Black powder is classified as an explosive and is easily ignited by heat, friction, static electricity or a sharp blow and must be handled with **extreme care**. It is strongly recommended that individuals interested in muzzleloading seek additional training from qualified specialists in the field.

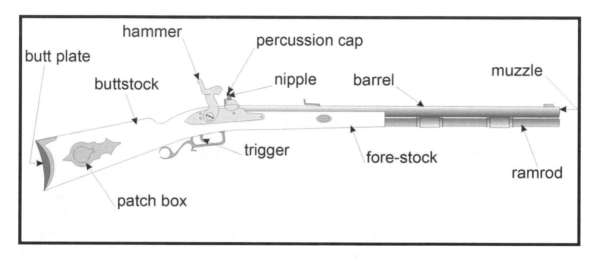

Figure 8. Muzzleloader

⚠ **Older firearms should be inspected by a qualified gunsmith to be sure they can be fired safely.**

2.2.1. Loading muzzleloaders

a. Today, most firearms for black powder use are reproductions of muzzleloaders. Older firearms may not be safe to fire and should be checked by a gunsmith before use.

b. If a muzzleloader is not primed to fire, it is safer to handle. To ensure that a muzzleloader is not primed to fire, do the following:

1. Point the muzzle in the safest available direction and keep finger off the trigger and out of the trigger guard.

2. Check that the hammer is **not** in full-cock position.

3. Check for a percussion cap or see if the priming pan is primed.

4. If the firearm is primed, remove cap or priming powder.

c. In addition, it is difficult to tell if there is already a charge loaded into the barrel of a muzzleloader. Experienced shooters mark the firearm's ramrod at a level that shows the bore depth when the bore is empty (Figure 9). When the marked ramrod is inserted into the barrel, it shows whether or not the firearm is loaded.

For other models of muzzleloading firearms, check with the manufacturer for specific safety features and information regarding the loading and unloading process.

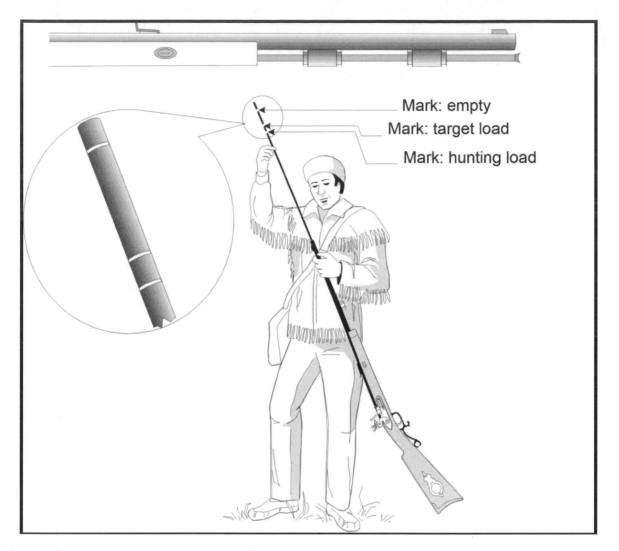

Mark: empty

Mark: target load

Mark: hunting load

Figure 9. Correctly Marked Ramrod

⚠️ In the case of muzzleloading firearms that have a safety catch, activate the safety catch before loading it. Prior to loading the firearm, use a cleaning rod with a fitted patch to check the gun bore and fire cap to ensure that nothing obstructs the chamber and gun bore. It is very important that the exact loading and unloading procedures are followed when handling muzzleloaders (Figures 10 and 11). Before attempting it, get the assistance of a qualified individual and carefully follow the instructions in your owner's manual.

CONSULT THE MANUFACTURER'S RECOMMENDATIONS.

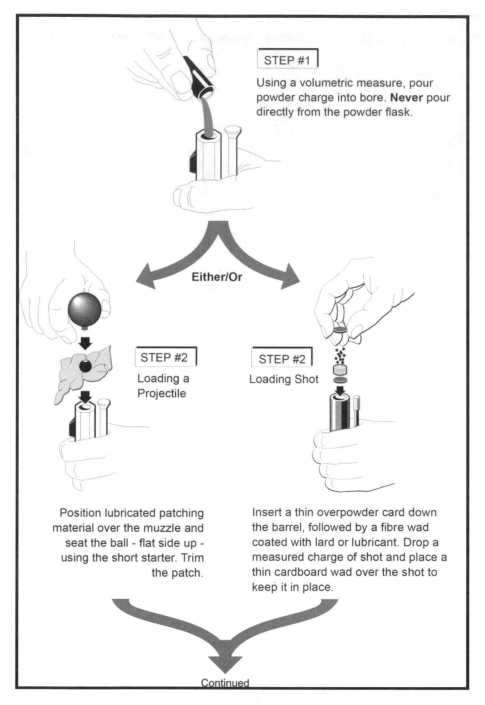

STEP #1

Using a volumetric measure, pour powder charge into bore. **Never** pour directly from the powder flask.

Either/Or

STEP #2

Loading a Projectile

STEP #2

Loading Shot

Position lubricated patching material over the muzzle and seat the ball - flat side up - using the short starter. Trim the patch.

Insert a thin overpowder card down the barrel, followed by a fibre wad coated with lard or lubricant. Drop a measured charge of shot and place a thin cardboard wad over the shot to keep it in place.

Continued

Figure 10. Loading a Muzzleloader

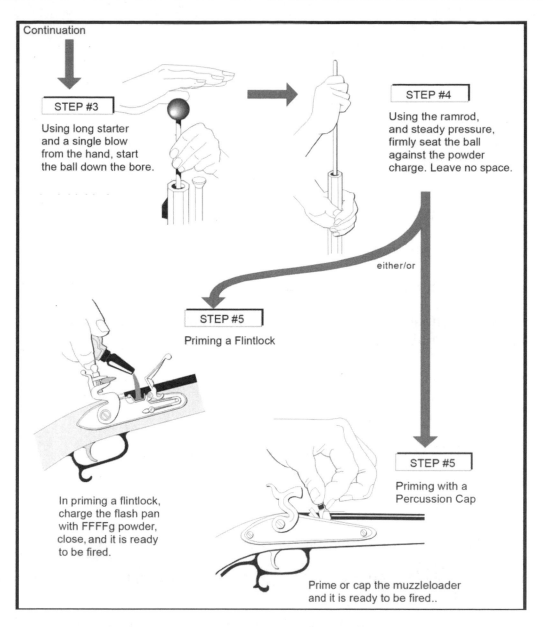

Figure 11. Loading a Muzzleloader *(cont'd)*

⚠ **Always use the powder recommended for your muzzleloader. Never use smokeless powder in a muzzleloader. Never use black powder in a modern cartridge firearm not designed for it. Always use a volumetric measure to put powder into the muzzle; never pour directly from the main powder container. Under safe-storage regulations, black-powder firearms are considered loaded when powder and/or ball are in the barrel.**

2.2.2 Cleaning a muzzleloader

a. ACTS and PROVE.

b. A black-powder firearm must be properly cleaned after every firing session. Black powder is very corrosive. It attracts moisture, which causes rust. Refer to the owner's manual.

c. Cleaning black-powder firearms improperly can result in carbon build-up in the barrel, which may cause **coking** (carbon accumulation). This condition may cause a glowing ember to remain after firing, resulting in a dangerous situation if the firearm is reloaded.

d. Use either commercial black powder cleaning solvent or hot, soapy water.

e. You will also need a ramrod with a cleaning patch attached. Use a rod as close to the bore diameter as possible.

f. Use wet patches to soften the dried powder.

2.2.3. DOs and DON'Ts of muzzleloading

*   **Do** have old muzzleloading firearms dismantled, examined and declared safe by a qualified gunsmith before using them.

*   **Do** handle the muzzleloader with the same respect due all firearms.

*   **Do** use ONLY black powder or black powder substitutes (e.g., Pyrodex) in your muzzleloader.

*   **Do** keep black powder far away from all cigarettes, matches/wicks or anything with an open flame, embers or anything that may cause sparks or heat.

*   **Do** always use a powder measure to pour powder directly into the muzzle. Never use the powder horn or flask.

*   **Do** carefully follow the manufacturer's recommendations for maximum powder charge.

*   **Do** mark your ramrod to indicate when the barrel is empty and when it is loaded.

*   **Do** wipe the bore clean of oil and excess grease **before** you load.

*   **Do** make sure the ball or bullet is seated firmly on the powder charge.

- **Do** treat a misfire as a hangfire that could fire at any second. Wait at least 60 seconds with the firearm pointed in a safe direction.

- **Do** wear safety glasses and hearing protection during the firing sequence.

- **Do** reseat your second charge after firing and reloading a single barrel on a multiple-barrel black-powder firearm. Recoil can move the charge forward.

- **Don't** carry or handle a muzzleloading firearm with the hammer at full cock and primed unless you are ready to fire.

- **Don't** lean over or stand in front of the muzzle at any time.

- **Don't** load one barrel of a double-barrelled-muzzleloading shotgun unless the percussion cap on the nipple of the other barrel has been removed.

- **Don't** store a muzzleloader with powder in it.

Subject to provincial/territorial regulations, loaded muzzleloading firearms **may** be carried from one hunting ground to another if the firing cap or flint is removed.

Black powder is also used in some metallic cartridges for firearms specifically designed for their use. Care should be taken. Although they have the same name as a modern smokeless cartridge, they may not be interchangeable. Never interchange smokeless powder and black powder. Use them only in firearms intended for their use.

2.3. Review questions

1. What type of powder is safe to use in muzzleloaders?

2. Is it safe to pour powder into a muzzleloader directly from a powder horn?

3. What component is used to check for a loaded chamber in a muzzleloader?

4. What is the wait time for a "hangfire" when using a muzzleloader?

5. List two items of personal protective gear that must be worn when firing a muzzleloader.

6. When do you cock the hammer during the loading and firing sequence of a muzzleloader?

MODULE 3:

MAJOR FIREARMS PARTS

MODULE 3: MAJOR FIREARMS PARTS

3.1. Major firearms parts

3.1.0. Overview

a. To use a firearm safely, you must know its parts and understand how they work. The following is a brief introduction to the parts of a firearm. Their functions are explained in more detail in MODULE 6: OPERATING FIREARMS ACTIONS.

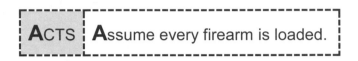

> **A**CTS   **A**ssume every firearm is loaded.

b. Modern firearms consist of three major parts: the barrel, the action and the stock (Figures 12 and 13).

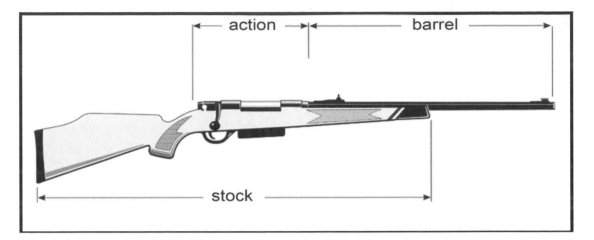

Figure 12. Bolt-action Rifle

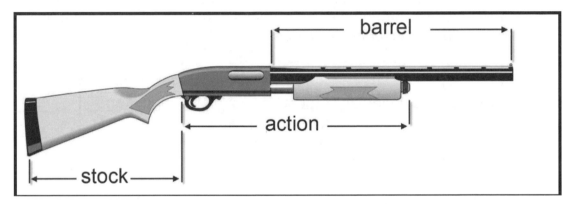

Figure 13. Pump-action Shotgun

3.1.1. Barrel

a. The *barrel* is a tube, typically made of metal. The bullet or shot travels down this tube when the firearm is fired.

b. Often, manufacturers identify cartridge information that is required for that firearm on the barrel—this is called the data stamp.

c. The opening at the end of the barrel from which the bullet or shot emerges is called the muzzle.

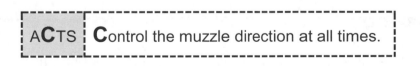

ACTS   Control the muzzle direction at all times.

3.1.2. Action

The *action* contains the parts that do the following:

- chamber the cartridge;

- fire the ammunition; and

- eject the unfired cartridges and fired cartridge/shell casings.

3.1.3 Trigger

a. *Triggers, safeties* and *magazines* are all parts of the action.

b. The *trigger* releases the hammer or firing pin that fires the cartridge. The *trigger guard* is a rigid loop around the trigger made to protect it and prevent anything from unintentionally touching the trigger.

AC**T**S	**T**rigger finger must be kept off the trigger and out of the trigger guard.

3.1.4. Safeties

a. *Safeties* usually block some part of the action to prevent firing. Some firearms do not have safeties.

b. The safety should be **ON / SAFETY POSITION** whenever a firearm is loaded. It should only be moved to **OFF / FIRING POSITION** when required.

c. Some safeties may also act as decocking levers.

⚠ **Never rely on the safety to prevent firing. A loaded firearm with the safety ON could still fire. All mechanical devices can fail—safeties can wear down and may not operate properly.**

3.1.5. Magazine

a. The *magazine* is a device that holds cartridges in repeating firearms. The location of the magazine depends on the make and model of the firearm.

b. The magazine can be either fixed or removed.

3.1.6. Stock

a. The *stock* is the handle of the firearm. Most are made of wood or a synthetic material.

b. Stocks are designed to automatically align your finger with the trigger when you pick up the firearm. You must be ever cautious not to put your finger into the trigger guard or on the trigger of a firearm that you are picking up.

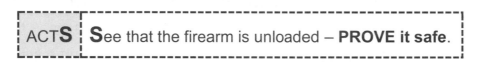

ACT**S** | **S**ee that the firearm is unloaded – **PROVE it safe**.

3.1.7. PROVE it safe

Table 4. PROVE it safe

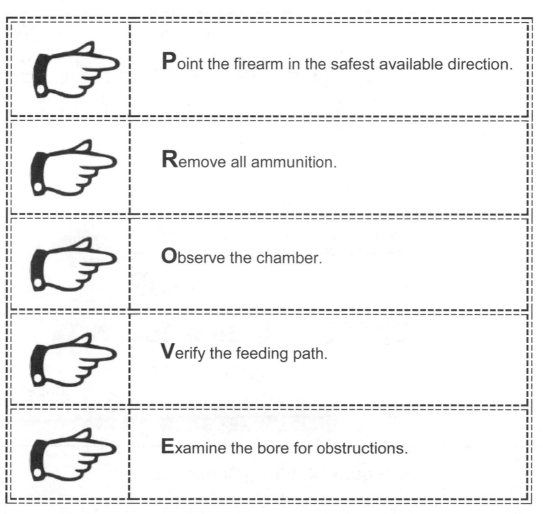

Point the firearm in the safest available direction.

Remove all ammunition.

Observe the chamber.

Verify the feeding path.

Examine the bore for obstructions.

The firearm is now unloaded and safe until it leaves the direct control of the person who unloaded and PROVEd it safe.

3.2. The firing sequence

Almost all modern firearms follow the same firing sequence (Figure 14):

1. A squeeze on the trigger releases the firing mechanism. This results in the firing pin striking the primer of the cartridge.

2. When struck by the firing pin, the primer explodes. This projects a flame into the cartridge body.

3. The flame from the primer ignites the powder. The powder burns and produces rapidly expanding gases.

4. The high-pressure gas drives the bullet or shot forward down the barrel.

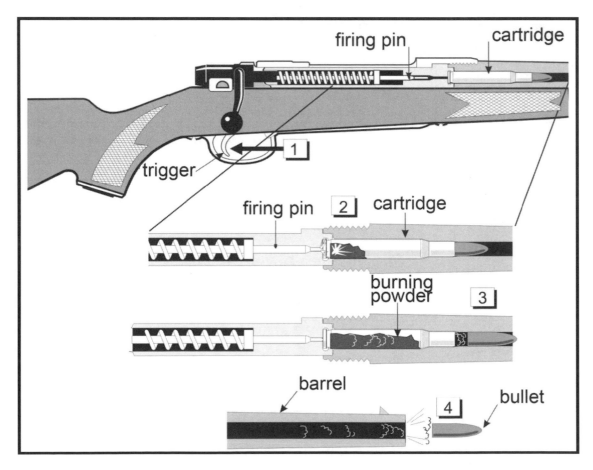

Figure 14. Firing Sequence

3.3. Action types

a. Firearms vary in design, depending on their purpose. Some are made for target shooting. Others are used for hunting birds or small game. Still others are for hunting big game.

b. The two common types of non-restricted firearms (long guns) are as follows:

- shotguns; and

- rifles.

c. The basic types of modern actions (Figure 15) used in these firearms are as follows:

- muzzleloader (percussion cap and flint) action;

- hinge (or break) action;

- bolt action;

- lever action;

- pump action; and

- semi-automatic action.

d. Some firearms have several barrels. Typically, these are shotguns or combination shotguns/rifles.

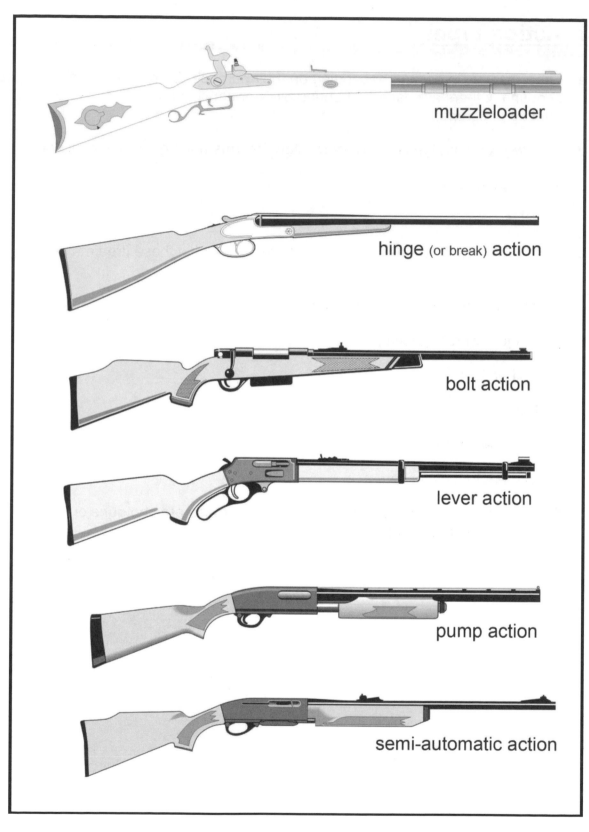

muzzleloader

hinge (or break) action

bolt action

lever action

pump action

semi-automatic action

Figure 15. Action Types

3.4. Classification of firearms

a. The classification of firearms is as follows:

- Non-restricted;

- Restricted; and

- Prohibited.

b. Legal requirements for a particular firearm depend on the class to which it belongs. Prohibited firearms are subject to the most stringent controls, restricted firearms are controlled to a lesser extent and non-restricted firearms are the least regulated of the three classes.

c. Many air guns, due to their high power, are included in the provisions of the *Firearms Act* and its Regulations. For this reason, all air guns must be treated as firearms with respect to safe practices, such as the **Vital Four ACTS of Firearm Safety**. Some models are considered firearms and must be registered like regular firearms.

⚠ **The Vital Four ACTS of Firearm Safety and PROVE apply to all classes of firearms.**

3.5. Legal responsibilities

⚠ **Various laws, regulations and restrictions govern your activities as an owner/user of a firearm. They set minimum standards of conduct, and you have both a legal and a social responsibility to understand and obey them.**

3.6. Review questions

1. List three major parts of a non-restricted firearm.

2. Give the meanings of "safety on" and "safety off."

3. Explain the firing sequence of a firearm.

4. List the two common types of non-restricted firearms.

5. Identify the six basic types of non-restricted firearms actions.

6. List the three classes of firearms.

7. All air, spring or gas firearms must be treated like firearms and must apply ACTS/PROVE. True or false?

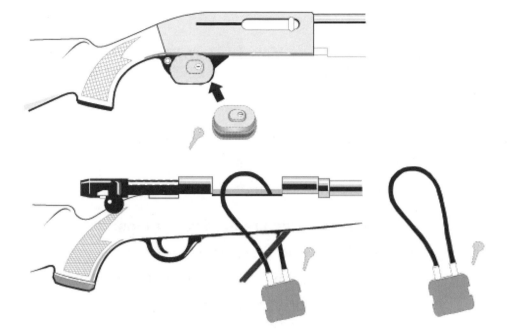

MODULE 4:

BASIC FIREARM SAFETY

MODULE 4: BASIC FIREARM SAFETY

4.1. Overview

Almost all firearm incidents can be prevented by following some basic safety rules. The most important of these are the **Vital Four ACTS of Firearm Safety** (Table 5) and **PROVE it safe** (Table 6). You may want to think of these rules as acts you must carry out.

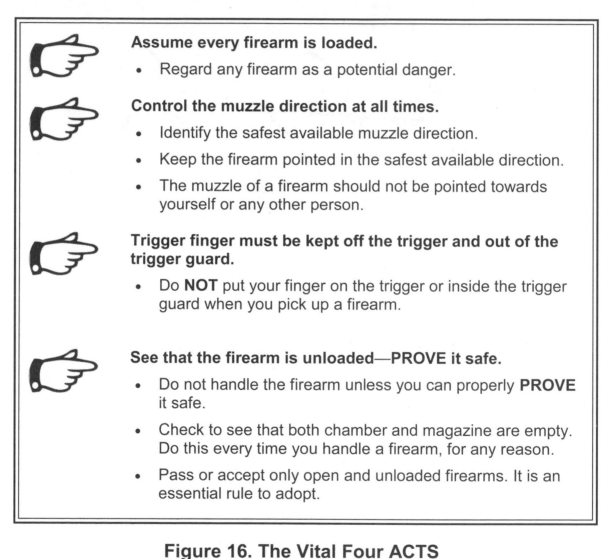

Assume every firearm is loaded.

- Regard any firearm as a potential danger.

Control the muzzle direction at all times.

- Identify the safest available muzzle direction.

- Keep the firearm pointed in the safest available direction.

- The muzzle of a firearm should not be pointed towards yourself or any other person.

Trigger finger must be kept off the trigger and out of the trigger guard.

- Do **NOT** put your finger on the trigger or inside the trigger guard when you pick up a firearm.

See that the firearm is unloaded—PROVE it safe.

- Do not handle the firearm unless you can properly **PROVE** it safe.

- Check to see that both chamber and magazine are empty. Do this every time you handle a firearm, for any reason.

- Pass or accept only open and unloaded firearms. It is an essential rule to adopt.

Figure 16. The Vital Four ACTS

STUDENT HANDBOOK – 2014

👉	**P**oint the firearm in the safest available direction.
👉	**R**emove all ammunition.
👉	**O**bserve the chamber.
👉	**V**erify the feeding path.
👉	**E**xamine the bore for obstructions.

Figure 17. PROVE it safe

The firearm is now unloaded and safe until it leaves the direct control of the person who unloaded and PROVEd it safe.

4.2. Basic firearm safety practices

4.2.0. Overview

While many safety practices have been incorporated into the *Firearms Act* and its Regulations, experienced firearm users often exceed those requirements by following some or all of the recommended safety practices listed in the following sections. These safety practices are summarized in Table 8 in Module 10.5. (For specific requirements on storage and transport, see MODULE 11: SAFE STORAGE, DISPLAY, TRANSPORTATION AND HANDLING OF NON-RESTRICTED FIREARMS.)

4.2.1. Firearms and ammunition safety practices

Some of the safety practices are listed below:

- All firearms and ammunition under your control are your responsibility 24 hours a day.

- Firearms are safer when stored and transported under lock and key. Examples include trigger or cable locks, and securely locked containers.

- In many cases, you are required by law to have your firearm unloaded and properly locked. Be aware of what the law says about which firearms need to be locked and when.

- Keep firearms and ammunition out of sight during transport and storage. This will reduce the chances of theft. It will also prevent unqualified or unauthorized persons from using them.

- Ammunition and firearms must be kept away from unsupervised children. Unlawful storage of firearms is a criminal offence that can lead to tragedy and serious consequences for the person found to be responsible.

- Store firearms unloaded. Lock the firearm and the ammunition separately when storing them or lock them in a secure container, receptacle or room that cannot be easily broken into.

4.2.2. Load a firearm only for actual use

Some of the safety practices are listed below:

- A firearm should be loaded only when you intend to use it and where it can be safely and legally discharged. At all other times, it should be unloaded.

- At the firing range, load a firearm only when you have reached the shooting area and you are ready to shoot. Completely unload the firearm before you leave the shooting area.

- Always make sure a firearm is unloaded before you pass it to anyone or anytime it leaves your hands. Whenever possible, leave the action open.

- Never accept a loaded firearm from anyone.

- Never run with a loaded firearm. Never climb or cross an obstacle with a loaded firearm. Never jump a ditch with a loaded firearm.

- Never toss or drop a firearm across a ditch or fence.

- Do not lean loaded firearms against a vehicle, tree or wall. They could fall over and discharge.

- Transport only unloaded firearms by vehicle or boat. Many incidents occur as firearms are being stored or removed from a vehicle. The motion of the vehicle or boat can make you stumble or drop the firearm. Either way, it can fire unintentionally if it is loaded.

- Always unload a firearm before transport or storage. This prevents unintentional discharge if the firearm is bumped during transport. It also reduces the chances of unexpected firing by an unqualified user.

4.2.3. Be sure before you shoot

Some of the safety practices are listed below:

Always use your firearm in the safest manner possible. Be sure of your target and beyond before you shoot.

- **Always examine the bore for obstructions before loading.**

- **Always check that you are using the right ammunition. Use only the ammunition for which the firearm was designed. Carry only the type of ammunition you intend to shoot.**

- **Never rely on the firearm's safety. Safeties wear down and may not work properly. A loaded firearm may fire even with the safety on. All mechanical devices can fail.**

4.2.4. Be sure of your target and beyond

a. To be sure of your target and beyond, follow the recommendations below:

- Positively identify your target. Make sure it is exactly what you want to shoot.

- Do not shoot when in doubt. Never fire at a movement, a colour, a sound or a shape.

- Check that you have a clear field of fire.

- Check that the area behind your target is safe before shooting.

- Never use a scope as a substitute for binoculars to identify persons, animals or objects.

b. Always be aware of where your bullet or shot may end up. This is your responsibility. A bullet or shot may ricochet. It may also travel far beyond the target. If you are unsure, check the following recommendations:

- Never shoot if your bullet may hit a hard surface or water. Both can cause a bullet or fragments to ricochet in unsafe directions.

- Never shoot at a target near a building.

- Never shoot at a target on top of a hill.

- Only shoot when you are sure no one is ahead of you.

4.3. Secure locking devices

a. Secure locking devices (Figure 18) prevent a firearm from being fired. To work effectively, they must be installed properly. Please note that not all secure locking devices are compatible with each firearm.

b. In some cases, they are required by law (MODULE 11: SAFE STORAGE, DISPLAY, TRANSPORTATION AND HANDLING OF NON-RESTRICTED FIREARMS). Several devices are available for this purpose. The most common are key and combination trigger locks, and chain or cable locks. All of these locks block operation. Check with a firearms dealer for a locking device best suited for your specific firearm.

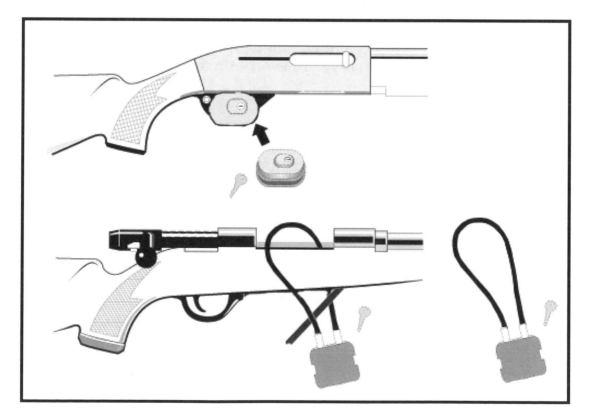

Figure 18. Various Firearm Locking Devices

61

4.4. Review questions

1. Describe four situations that constitute a dangerous background when shooting.

2. Should you use a scope to glass the terrain, locate and identify your target?

3. Can the safety mechanism on your firearm be relied upon?

4. Is it safe to accept a loaded firearm from a friend?

5. Is it best practice for three friends with different calibre rifles to transport their ammunition on the dash of a pickup truck?

MODULE 5:

AMMUNITION

MODULE 5: AMMUNITION

5.0. Overview

This module discusses rifle cartridges and shotgun shells. This will help you choose the right ammunition. You should only carry ammunition that suits the firearm that you are using and the target that you intend to shoot. This applies whether you are hunting or target shooting.

For more detailed information, consult a firearms vendor or a gunsmith.

5.1. Rifling

a. Rifled barrels have a series of spiral grooves inside the barrel. The ridges of metal between the grooves are called lands. The lands and grooves together make up the rifling (Figure 19).

b. Rifling makes the bullet spin as it leaves the barrel so that it will be stable in flight, thus making the bullet more accurate.

5.2. Calibre

a. Rifled firearms are sized by calibre. A calibre is a measurement of bore diameter in either thousands of an inch (Imperial) or in millimetres (Metric). Inch dimensions are usually measured from land to land, while metric dimensions are measured from groove to groove.

⚠ **Always consult the data stamp on the barrel of your firearm to find out the exact name of the ammunition that fits it.**

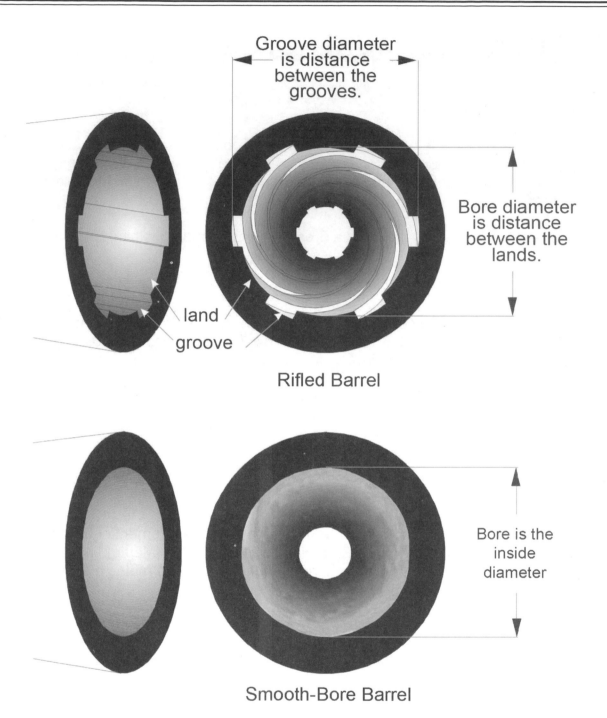

Figure 19. Rifled Bore and Smooth Bore

5.3. Cartridges

5.3.0. Overview

a. A cartridge is the ammunition used in a rifle or a handgun. Two kinds of cartridges commonly available are: rim-fire and centre-fire. These terms describe where the primer is located at the base of the cartridge casing. They also describe where the firing pin strikes (Figure 18).

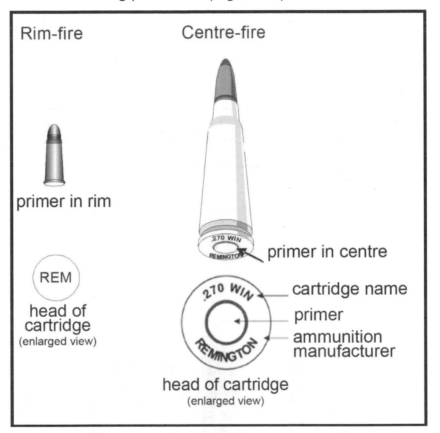

Figure 20. Examples of a Rim-fire and a Centre-fire Cartridge with Head Stamp

b. Manufacturers produce firearms of many calibres. **Always make sure the cartridge name on the "head stamp" matches the information on the data stamp**, if available, on the barrel of the firearm (Figure 20). This is the most important point to remember when selecting ammunition. Then, choose the right type of ammunition for your firearm and target. The right shape or weight of the bullet is an example. If in doubt, consult a firearms or ammunition vendor.

c. If there is no data stamp, take the firearm to a qualified individual. They can measure the chamber and advise on proper ammunition.

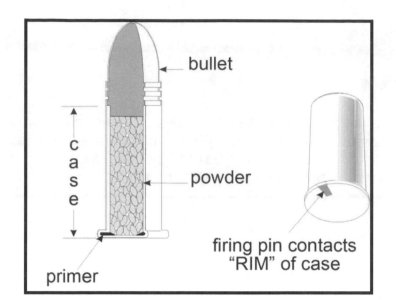

Figure 21. Rim-fire Cartridge

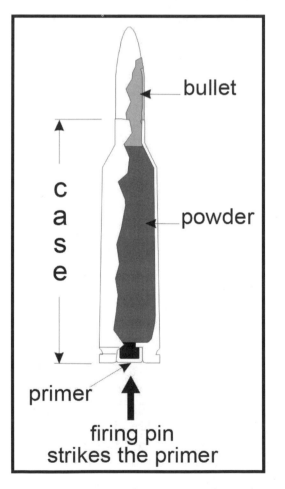

Figure 22. Centre-fire Cartridge

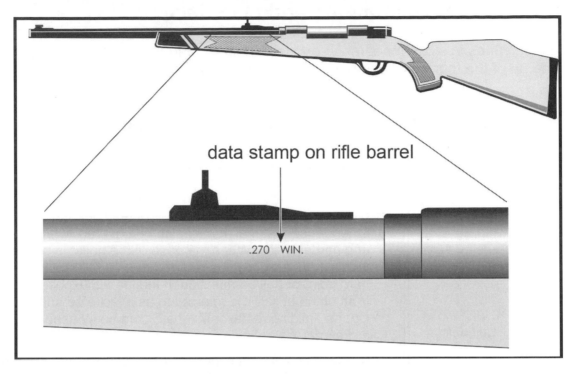

data stamp on rifle barrel

.270   WIN.

Figure 23. Example of a Barrel Data Stamp

⚠ Use caution when purchasing used firearms. Some firearms may not have a data stamp, or they may have an incorrect stamp. Some firearms may have been altered and the existing data stamp may be incorrect. They should be checked by a qualified individual before use.

If you are reloading your own ammunition, you must strictly follow the instructions and procedures outlined in the manuals provided for this process. Visually inspect all cartridge components for defects before loading.

d. Many firearm owners load their own centre-fire ammunition. This allows them to save money and create a high-quality product made specifically for their firearm and shooting conditions. If you load your own ammunition, you must rigorously follow the instructions and procedures indicated in the relating manuals.

e. Incorrectly loaded ammunition may cause the firearm to malfunction or jam. Malfunctions could lead to an incident. The firearm could explode and injure the shooter. Do not accept or use reloaded cartridges unless you know that they were made and reloaded correctly.

5.3.1. Cartridge components and materials

Ammunition varies in size, appearance and materials. Ammunition cartridges for rifles are made up of the four basic components described below (Figure 24).

Table 5. Cartridge Components and Materials

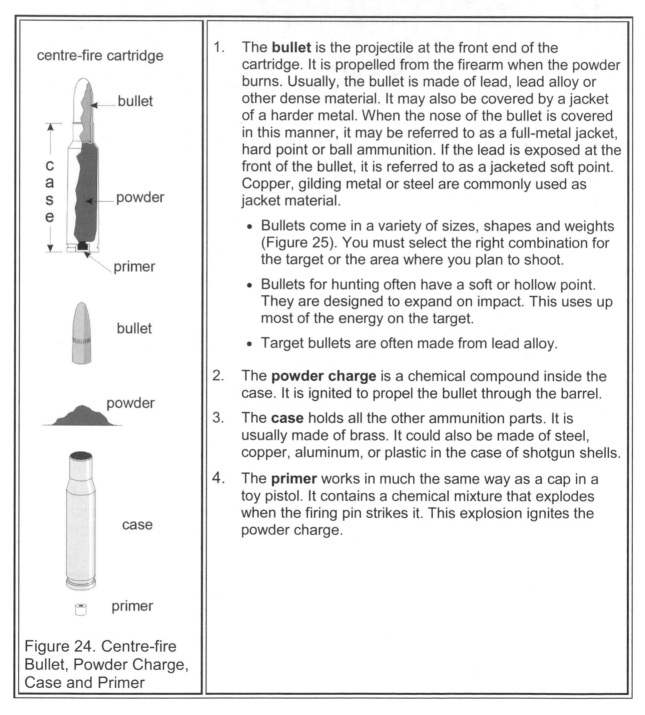

centre-fire cartridge

bullet

case

powder

primer

bullet

powder

case

primer

Figure 24. Centre-fire Bullet, Powder Charge, Case and Primer

1. The **bullet** is the projectile at the front end of the cartridge. It is propelled from the firearm when the powder burns. Usually, the bullet is made of lead, lead alloy or other dense material. It may also be covered by a jacket of a harder metal. When the nose of the bullet is covered in this manner, it may be referred to as a full-metal jacket, hard point or ball ammunition. If the lead is exposed at the front of the bullet, it is referred to as a jacketed soft point. Copper, gilding metal or steel are commonly used as jacket material.

    - Bullets come in a variety of sizes, shapes and weights (Figure 25). You must select the right combination for the target or the area where you plan to shoot.

    - Bullets for hunting often have a soft or hollow point. They are designed to expand on impact. This uses up most of the energy on the target.

    - Target bullets are often made from lead alloy.

2. The **powder charge** is a chemical compound inside the case. It is ignited to propel the bullet through the barrel.

3. The **case** holds all the other ammunition parts. It is usually made of brass. It could also be made of steel, copper, aluminum, or plastic in the case of shotgun shells.

4. The **primer** works in much the same way as a cap in a toy pistol. It contains a chemical mixture that explodes when the firing pin strikes it. This explosion ignites the powder charge.

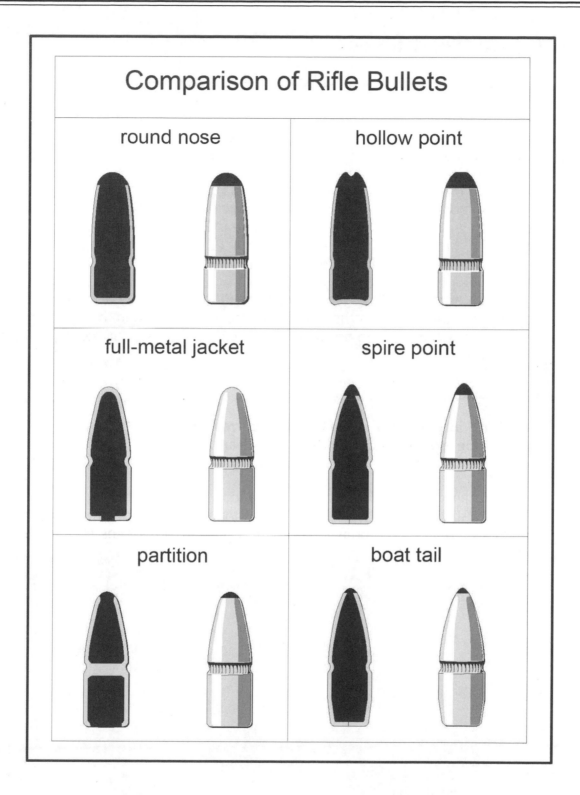

Figure 25. Comparison of Rifle Bullets

5.3.2. Types of cartridges

There are two basic types of modern cartridges: rim-fire and centre-fire.

a. **Rim-fire** ammunition's priming chemical fills the space inside the bottom rim of a thin brass or copper cartridge casing. The soft rim dents when struck by the firing pin. This crushes the priming compound. It explodes, and this ignites the powder (Figure 21).

- Popular modern rim-fire cartridges are .22 calibre or .17HMR. The most common is the .22 cartridge. It is available in BB, short and long rifle; however, it is not interchangeable with the .22 magnum cartridge. Be sure to use the correct ammunition for your specific firearm.

- Rim-fire cartridge bullets generally are made of lead. They are lubricated with grease or special waxes that reduce the build-up of lead in the rifle barrel. In some cases they can be encapsulated in copper that's a full-metal jacket (i.e., .17HMR).

 Dry firing any firearm can damage the firearm. Dry firing means to initiate the firing sequence without a cartridge in the chamber.

b. **Centre-fire** ammunition (Figure 22) is used for higher power firearms. The primer is located at the centre of the base of the cartridge case. The firing pin strikes the primer. This explodes the priming compound. This in turn ignites the powder charge.

5.3.3. Cartridge names

a. There are various ways of identifying or "naming" cartridges. Some cartridges have several names. The cartridge name, or an abbreviation of it, is stamped on the head of the case. It is also found printed on the ammunition manufacturer's box (Figure 26).

b. Historically, cartridge names contained their approximate calibres. Calibre refers to the diameter of the bore. Calibre may be measured in thousands of an inch or in metric.

c. Currently, modern firearms include the length of the cartridge casing in the description of the cartridge to identify the name of the ammunition that the firearm is designed to use. This is done to tell the difference between cartridges having the same calibre but different cartridge casings. **For example, cartridges with different names are not interchangeable (.303 Savage and .303 British, 7-mm Mauser and 7-mm Remington Magnum, .300 Savage and .300 Win Mag).**

d. A manufacturer may choose to make a firearm or ammunition in a cartridge originally made by another manufacturer, and as a result, confusion can occur. For example, you can use a Remington rifle to fire a .300 Winchester Magnum cartridge made by the Federal Cartridge Company.

e. The head stamp includes very valuable information, such as the cartridge name. It may also tell you the following:

- the calibre

- the manufacturer; and

- Whether the ammunition is regular or magnum and any other relevant details.

f. Always read the cartridge name. It is the only way to be sure that the cartridge matches the firearm. If in doubt, check with a gunsmith or gun shop.

g. The term magnum comes from the description of a large bottle of wine. It was first applied to large bottleneck cartridges that produced greater power than was the normal standard for that calibre. Today, it is more a marketing term than a technical term, but is an important part of the name.

Some ammunition may not have a cartridge name head stamp, such as rim-fire cartridges. Also, some privately reloaded ammunition may no longer match the original stamp. Whenever possible, refer to the information on the ammunition box. If in doubt, have any such ammunition checked by a qualified individual before you use it.

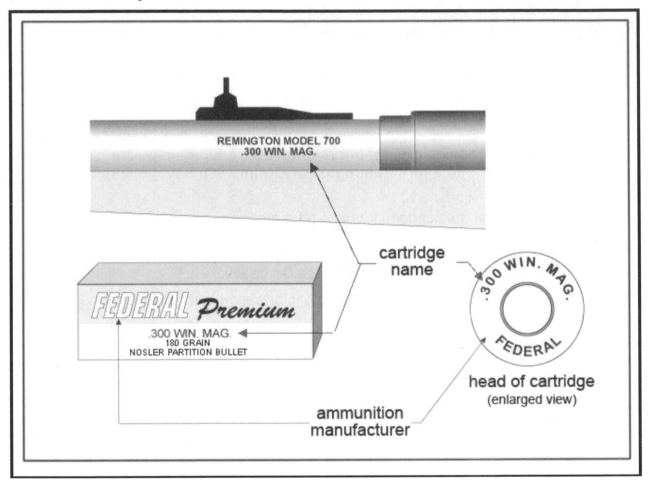

Figure 26. Data Stamp on Rifle Barrel

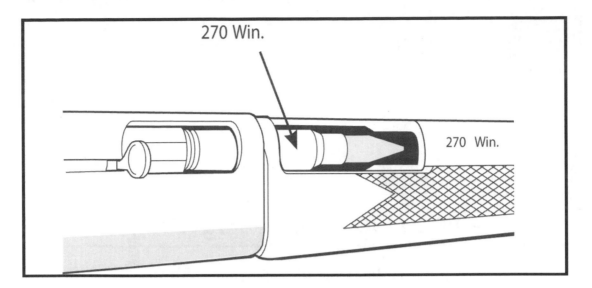

Figure 27. Cut-away of Ammunition Being Chambered in a Barrel

5.4. Shotgun barrels

a. The use of smooth slugs, rifled slugs, and slugs contained in a sabot or plastic sleeve, is becoming more common in modern shotguns (Figure 28). This allows shotguns to fire single projectiles (bullets).

b. Some shotguns were manufactured with adjustable chokes. Modern shotguns are made with interchangeable choke tubes. On these models, the choke can be changed simply by unscrewing a removable tube at the muzzle of the barrel and replacing it with another tube with a different choke.

c. A shotgun with interchangeable chokes or barrels can be used for skeet or clay target shooting, migratory waterfowl, upland game birds and large game hunting, depending on the ammunition used and the regulations in the area.

d. The rifled barrel is becoming popular. The rifled barrel provides the options of using a smooth slug, a rifled slug or a sabot slug. The rifled barrel is designed to make the projectiles spin as they leave the muzzle. This makes them more like a normal rifle bullet, increasing accuracy and useful distance.

e. Rifled shotgun barrels are identical to a normal rifle barrel except that they have the bore diameter of the gauge of the shotgun. This has resulted in better accuracy and new uses for shotguns.

Figure 28. Types of Shotgun Slugs

5.5. Shotgun gauge

Shotgun barrels are sized by gauge instead of calibre. Gauge is an older system of measurement and is calculated by the number of lead balls (each having the same diameter as the bore) that weigh one pound. In other words, if it took 12 balls with the same diameter as a bore to make one pound, a shotgun with that bore would be called a 12-gauge shotgun. One exception to this rule is the .410-cal. shotgun. It is measured as a calibre because it was developed later (Figure 29).

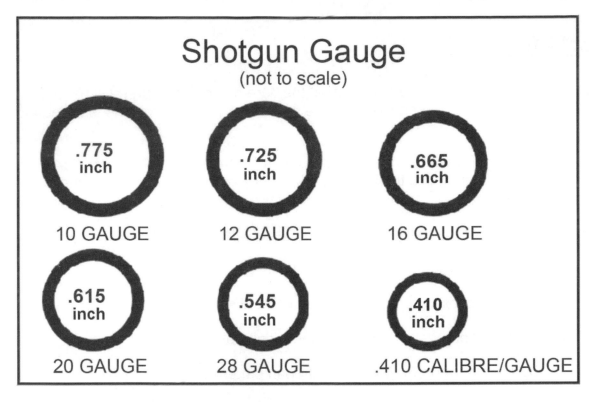

Figure 29. Shotgun Gauges

NOTES: 12 lead balls = 1 lb = 12 gauge
.410 is an imperial measure because of its American manufacture.

5.6. Choke

a. Except in the case of a rifled barrel, the bore of a shotgun barrel is usually smooth and may be narrowed at the muzzle end. This narrowing is called the choke.

b. The choke of a shotgun barrel helps control the spread of the shot after it is fired. This is very much like the way the nozzle of a garden hose controls the spray of water.

c. The pattern of the pellets on the target is affected by the choke:

- Full choke produces a tight pattern;

- Modified choke produces a more open pattern;

- Improved cylinder produces a more open pattern; and

- Cylinder bore produces the most open pattern.

d. A shotgun barrel which has no choke or narrowing at the end of the barrel is called a cylinder bore. It is often used for larger pellet sizes such as buckshot or slugs.

e. Most modern manufactured shotguns feature a screw-in choke that can be changed depending on the use of the shotgun.

See **Figure 30** for the uses of the various chokes and their shot patterns. The pattern will depend on the different type of shot used, for example: lead, steel, bismuth or tungsten-iron among others. It is the shooter's responsibility to learn about the shotgun pattern and to determine the pattern for their particular shotgun and ammunition.

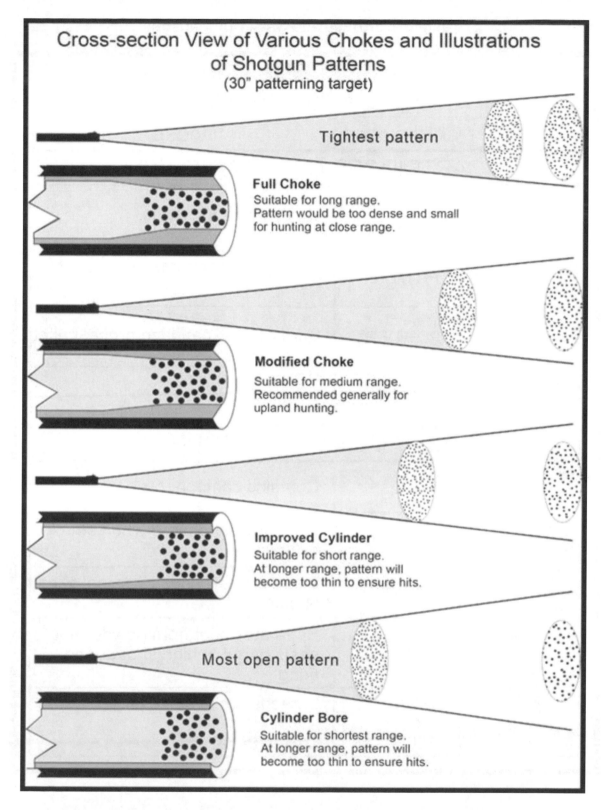

Figure 30. Cross-section View (Chokes and Patterns)

Table 6. Cartridge and Shell Comparison

Comparison of Rifle Cartridges to Shotgun Shells

TYPE	COMPONENTS	PURPOSE
CARTRIDGES USED IN RIFLES		
Rim-Fire or Centre-Fire Sizes: Calibre e.g. -.17HMR, .22, .30 or 7 mm	CASE	Contains components
	PRIMER	Fires powder charge when struck by firing pin
	POWDER	Burns and expands to propel bullet
	BULLET	Strikes target
SHELLS USED IN SHOTGUNS		
Sizes: Gauge e.g. - 12 or 20 gauge or .410 cal. 2¾", 3, 3½" approximate case length *after* firing.	HULL	Contains components
	PRIMER	Fires powder charge when struck by firing pin
	POWDER	Burns and expands to propel shot or slug
	WAD	Separates shot from powder and seals barrel behind shot during firing
	SHOT or SLUG	Spreads out to strike target Strikes target

5.7. Shotgun shells

5.7.0. Overview

a. Shotgun ammunition is centre-fire. The casing or hull has a thick, solid base. The primer is located in a separate cup in the centre bottom of the casing (Figure 31).

b. The firing pin strikes the primer. This explodes the priming compound and ignites the powder. The shot charge is usually a number of pellets. It can also be a single slug.

5.7.1. Shotgun shell components and materials

a. Shotgun shell components are similar to those of rifle cartridges. However, there are five components, not four (Figure 32). The five shotgun components are described below.

1. **Shot** is the name for the charge of pellets fired from a shotgun. Shot may be either lead, steel, bismuth or tungsten-iron pellets. Historically, shot was primarily made of lead. However, because of environmental concerns, use of other materials is increasing:

   • The use of steel in some shotgun barrels may cause damage to the firearms. For further information, please check the manufacturer's manual or contact a gunsmith.

   • The size and number of pellets vary. They depend on the type and range of the target. Smaller pellets are usually used for smaller or closer targets (see the Figure in Table 7).

   • Sometimes a single large projectile known as a **"slug"** is fired from a shotgun. This is for hunting larger game.

2. Shotgun shells also contain one or more **wads**. The wad is made of paper, fibre or plastic. It separates the powder charge from the shot or slug. This prevents hot gas from damaging the shot and seals the gases behind the charge. It also separates the shot from the inside of the barrel.

3. The **powder charge** is a chemical compound in the body of the hull. It is ignited to propel the shot through the barrel.

4. The **hull** contains all the other ammunition components. The hull is commonly made of a combination of brass, plastic or paper.

5. The **primer** contains a chemical mixture that explodes when the firing pin strikes it. This ignites the powder charge.

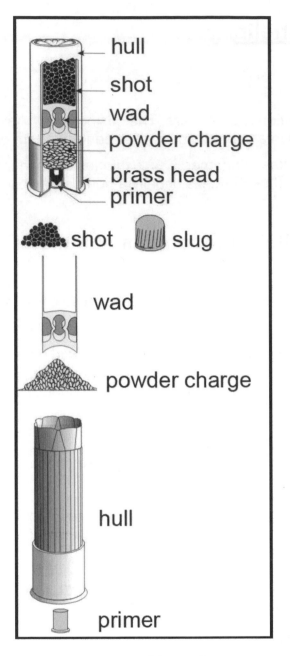

Figure 31. Shotgun Shell Components

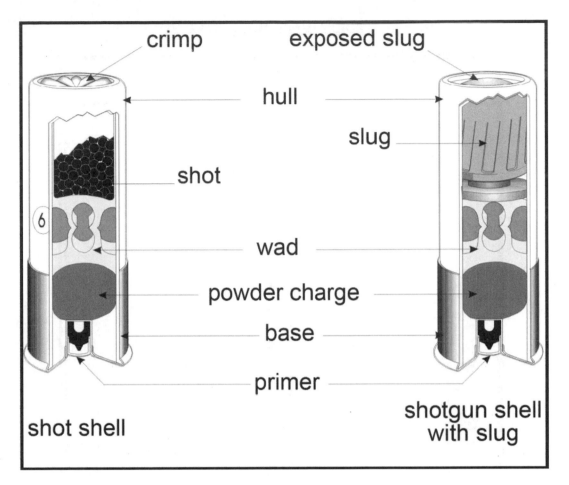

Figure 32. Shotgun Shells

Table 7. Lead Shot Sizes

Shot Sizes

Buckshot Sizes				Shot Sizes			
	Shot Number	Diameter in Inches	# Pellets Typical Loads		Shot Number	Diameter in Inches	Pellets / oz. Lead	Pellets / oz. Steel
	4	.24	27 34		9	.08	585	na
	3	.25	20 24		8	.09	410	na
	1	.30	12 16 20 24		7½	.095	350	na
	0	.32	12		7	.10	-	420
	00	.33	9 12 15		6	.11	225	316
	000	.36	8		5	.12	170	243
					4	.13	135	191
					3	.14	-	153
					2	.15	87	125
					1	.16	-	103
					B	.17	-	na
					BB	.18	50	72
					BBB	.19	-	61
					T	.20	-	53
					TT	.21	-	na
					F	.22	-	na

5.7.2. Shotgun shell types

1. Various types of shells exist. They vary in length, gauge, size and type of pellet (shot)—Table 7. To choose the right ammunition for your firearm and target, follow the manufacturer's recommendations. For example, shotgun shells in 12 gauge commonly come in several lengths as follows:

    *   70 mm (2¾ inches);

    *   76 mm (3 inches); and

    *   89 mm (3½ inches).

    NOTE: These dimensions refer to the lengths of the shells **after** firing (Figure 33).

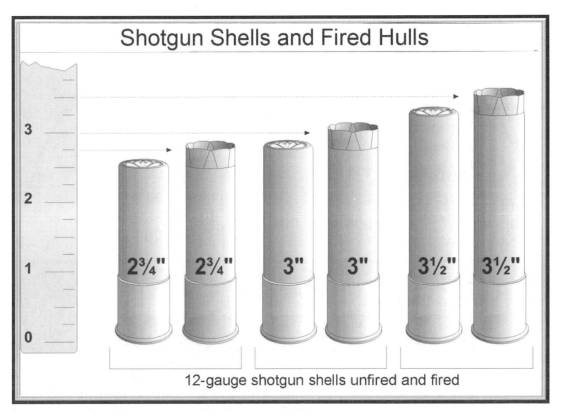

Figure 33. Shotgun Shells and Fired Hulls

⚠ **It should be noted that some European shotguns are manufactured in 2- and 2½ inch chamber size. Firing a 2¾-inch shell in these firearms is dangerous. Other lengths are possible in gauge other than 12 gauge. If in doubt, check with a gunsmith. Actual shell length may vary slightly from these sizes. Shell manufacturers round off the sizes shown on the boxes.**

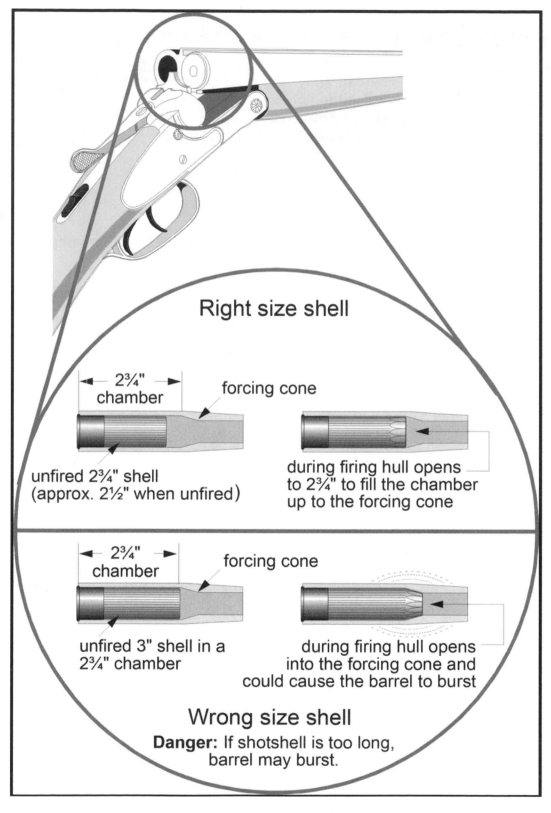

Figure 34. Shell in Chamber

a. The following information is stamped on the barrel or action (Figure 35) of many modern shotguns:

- gauge;

- maximum shell/chamber length; and

- type of choke.

b. The gauge of a shotgun shell is printed on the base of the shell. The gauge and the shell length are also on the ammunition manufacturer's box. This information must be matched to the data stamp on the shotgun barrel prior to loading the firearm. If in doubt, check with a gunsmith or a gun shop.

c. If there is no data stamp, take the firearm to a gunsmith. The gunsmith can measure the firearm and give advice on proper ammunition.

d. Chamber dimensions are given for a fired shell. Use the information on the box. If you measured an unfired shell, you might think a 3-inch shell is only 2¾ inches and have an incident.

 Do not attempt to use longer ammunition than indicated on the barrel data stamp. If you do, the barrel might burst (Figure 36).

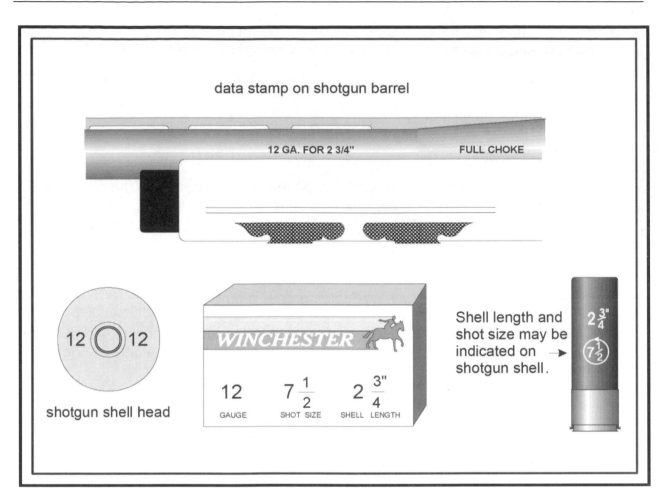

Figure 35. Data Stamp on Shotgun Shell

Serious injuries may occur when hunters or shooters load the wrong ammunition into their firearms. An easy mistake to make is loading and chambering a 20-gauge shotgun shell into a 12-gauge shotgun. The small shell will slide through the chamber and stick in the forcing cone. Users may then insert a 12-gauge shell behind the 20-gauge shell. When fired, the barrel may burst (Figure 36). Burst barrels scatter metal. People have been seriously injured or killed by this error.

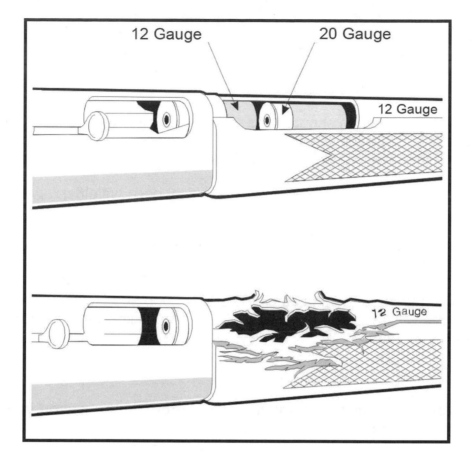

Figure 36. Exploded Chamber

For hunting, various provincial rules about shot and bullet size and materials exist. Your course instructor can provide more precise information. You can also check with your local hunting authority for exact regulations.

5.8. Ballistics

a. Ballistics is the study of projectiles in flight.

b. Modern firearms can shoot a long distance. For this reason, every shooter should understand ballistics. Shotguns can fire shot more than the length of a football field. Some rifles can fire bullets further than five kilometres.

c. A general knowledge of ballistics is important because different ammunition has different penetrating effects. A projectile may not stop where you want it to.

d. Ballistics tables for ammunition supply the information to calculate the flight path and performance of cartridges.

e. You want to hunt or shoot safely. Therefore, you need to know how far your projectile will travel. That means that you need to know the dangerous range (Figures 37 and 38).

 Be sure of your target and beyond. If there is any reason your shot may be unsafe, do not fire.

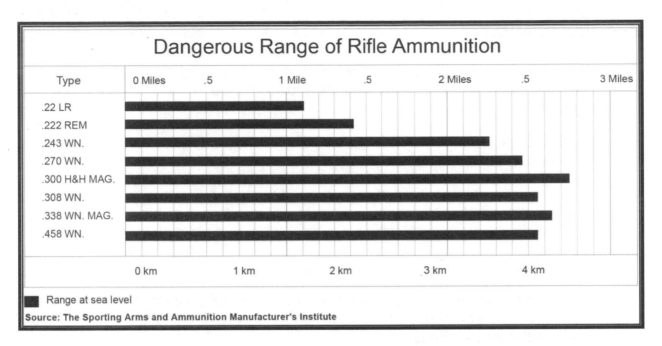

Figure 37. Dangerous Range of Rifle Ammunition

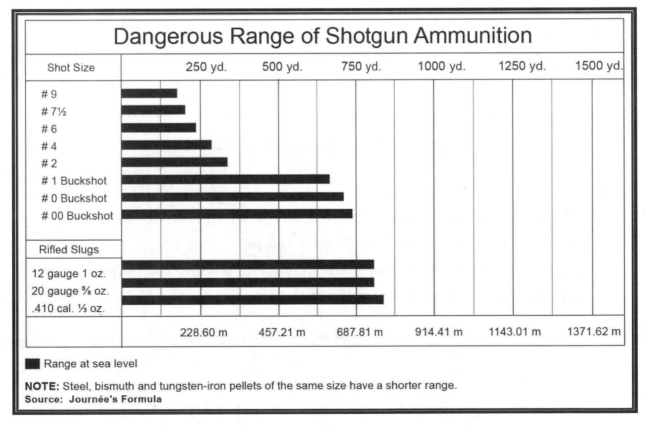

Figure 38. Dangerous Range of Shotgun Ammunition

5.9. Trajectory

a. The trajectory is the path a discharged shot or bullet takes during flight (Figure 39). Several factors affect this path; examples include, but are not limited to, the following:

- Gravity pulls the bullet down toward the ground as it is travelling forward. This results in a downward curved path.

- Air resistance holds back the passage of the bullet. This slows its flight.

- Velocity is the speed at which a bullet travels, in a given direction.

- Mass is the weight of the bullet.

b. The firearm muzzle must be raised from the horizontal position to make up for gravity. The trajectory of a projectile is slightly curved. It crosses the line of sight twice on the way to the target.

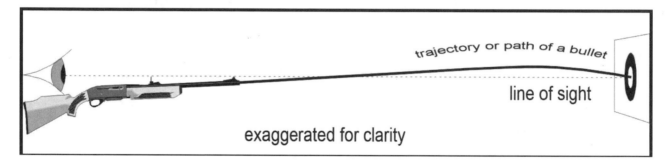

Figure 39. Trajectory of a Bullet

Responsible shooters will follow the recommendations below:

- **Only fire at targets within the effective range.**
- **Consider how far the shot or bullet may travel beyond the target.**
- **You are responsible for where the bullet stops.**

5.10. Hazards

The selection of the correct ammunition for the firearm is critical to safe operation. Modern commercial ammunition is normally very reliable but there are several ways the cartridge may not fire.

- A misfire is a cartridge that does not fire. Misfired cartridges should not be reused in the firearm and must be disposed of properly. Muzzleloading firearms may also misfire.

- A hangfire is a delayed fire in which the firing pin strikes the primer but it does not create enough flame to ignite the powder instantly. If the muzzle is not pointed in a safe direction when the cartridge eventually fires, it may result in an injury. If the cartridge is removed from the chamber and then discharges, the explosive rupture of the case may also cause injury. Muzzleloading firearms may also have a hangfire.

- A primer pop (squib load) happens when the cartridge does not contain any gunpowder. The firearms will discharge the primer without the usual noise or recoil. This may have enough force to push the bullet out of the case, but the bullet may lodge in the barrel. If another bullet is fired, the barrel may rupture and possibly cause injury.

If the trigger is pulled and there is no noticeable discharge, wait 60 seconds while pointing the muzzle in a safe direction. If there is no hangfire within 60 seconds, open the action pointing away from yourself and unload the firearm. PROVE the firearm safe to ensure there is no blockage lodged in the barrel.

5.11. Firearm malfunctions

Generally, when using commercially made ammunition and a properly maintained firearm, malfunctions will not occur. Firearms jammed with a cartridge or shell in the chamber(s) can be a hazard and must be carefully cleared of the jam. This hazard, if not dealt with properly, may result in a serious injury. Consult a qualified person or gunsmith for information on how to perform this function in the safest possible manner.

5.12. Ammunition precautions and legislation

Explosives information is issued by Natural Resources Canada. It indicates that you may keep reasonable quantities of sporting ammunition on your property. "Reasonable" means quantities typically required for a rifle or shotgun, or for part of a collection. This ammunition must be for your private use, not resale. Contact Natural Resources Canada for details. You must take every necessary precaution against incidents by adhering to the instructions below:

- Ammunition must be stored out of children's reach. It must be kept away from flammables.

- Ammunition for a non-restricted firearm may only be stored in a place where it is not within easy access to the firearm, unless the ammunition is stored, together with or separately from the firearm, in a securely locked container or receptacle that cannot be easily broken open or into.

- Ammunition for a non-restricted firearm must not be displayed with the firearm or be within easy access to the firearm from which it can be discharged.

- All ammunition should be stored in a cool, dry place, preferably in a vented container. This will reduce the chance of corrosion or breakdown of the ammunition components that could cause the firearm to jam or misfire.

> See below for a summary of **"Ammunition Safety Points to Remember"**.

⚠ **Keep in mind that storing ammunition in an unvented container may create an explosive hazard during a fire.**

Ammunition Safety Points to Remember

- Carry ammunition only for the firearm you are using.

- Never experiment with unfamiliar ammunition.

- Using modern ammunition in old firearms may be hazardous.

- When a misfire occurs, slowly count to 60 while pointing the muzzle in a safe direction. Remove the cartridge following safe procedures. Then, carefully inspect the bore for obstructions.

- Never use old or corroded ammunition or reloading components.

- Never use cartridges if you are uncertain about their safe use.

- Never interchange smokeless powder and black powder. Use them only in firearms intended for their use.

- Store all ammunition so that unauthorized persons do not have access to it.

- Ammunition should never be displayed with a firearm.

- Ammunition is most safely carried in its original container.

- When hand loading your own ammunition, be certain to strictly follow the procedures in the manuals about reloading ammunition. Treat primers with extra caution—they are explosive devices.

5.13. Review questions

1. Under what circumstances can you store ammunition with a firearm?

2. Name the malfunction whereby, after the trigger is pulled, there is a several-second delay before firing.

3. What is the preferred temperature and humidity for ammunition storage?

4. Describe four factors which affect trajectory.

5. What safety precaution should be taken with a firearm that does not have a data stamp?

6. Is it legal to display a firearm and its ammunition together?

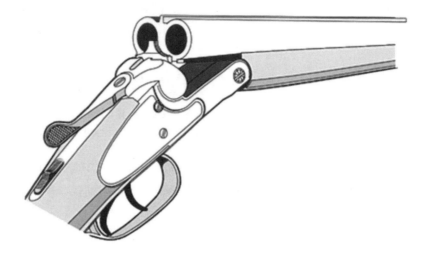

MODULE 6:

OPERATING FIREARMS ACTIONS

MODULE 6: OPERATING FIREARMS ACTIONS

6.0. Overview

a. To understand the safe use of firearms, you must become familiar with action types, how they work, and how to safely load and unload them.

b. This module first defines the different types of firearms, various safeties and action releases and shows how to do the following:

- identify each type of action;

- locate safeties (some actions will not open unless the safety is **OFF**);

- pick up a gun—**ACTS** and **PROVE it safe**; and

- safely load each type of action, with the safety **ON**, whenever possible.

⚠ **Always wear safety glasses and hearing protection when loading and discharging firearms.**

The Vital Four ACTS of Firearm Safety

Assume every firearm is loaded.

- Regard any firearm as a potential danger.

Control the muzzle direction at all times.

- Identify the safest available muzzle direction.

- Keep the firearm pointed in the safest available direction.

- The muzzle of a firearm should not be pointed towards yourself or any other person.

Trigger finger must be kept off the trigger and out of the trigger guard.

- Do **NOT** put your finger on the trigger or inside the trigger guard when you pick up a firearm.

See that the firearm is unloaded—PROVE it safe.

- Do not handle the firearm unless you can properly **PROVE it safe**.

- Check to see that both chamber and magazine are empty. Do this every time you handle a firearm, for any reason.

- Pass or accept only open and unloaded firearms. It is an essential rule to adopt.

PROVE it safe

PROVE is an acronym, or memory aid, that stands for the five steps required to ensure that a firearm is unloaded and safe. The five steps are: **P**oint, **R**emove, **O**bserve, **V**erify and **E**xamine. These procedures must be followed to safely unload any firearm.

1. **P**oint the firearm in the safest available direction.

2. **R**emove all ammunition.

3. **O**bserve the chamber(s).

4. **V**erify the feeding path.

5. **E**xamine the bore(s).

⚠ **The firearm is now unloaded and safe until it leaves the direct control of the person who unloaded and PROVEd it safe. Direct control is defined as having the firearm within eyesight and/or arm's reach of the shooter.**

6.1. Action types

Firearms are generally classified by their type of action. There are six basic types (Figure 40).

- A muzzleloader is loaded through the muzzle with black powder or black powder substitutes. Ignition is created by the flash produced by the hammer striking a percussion cap.

- A hinge (or break) action opens near the breech and is usually single- or double-barreled.

- A bolt action is similar to a door bolt and can be single or multiple shot.

- A lever action has a metal handle that opens the action. It can be single or multiple shot.

- A pump action works by pumping the fore-end of the stock back and forth and is normally multiple shots.

- A semi-automatic action extracts and ejects empty casings and inserts another cartridge in the chamber automatically, each time you pull the trigger.

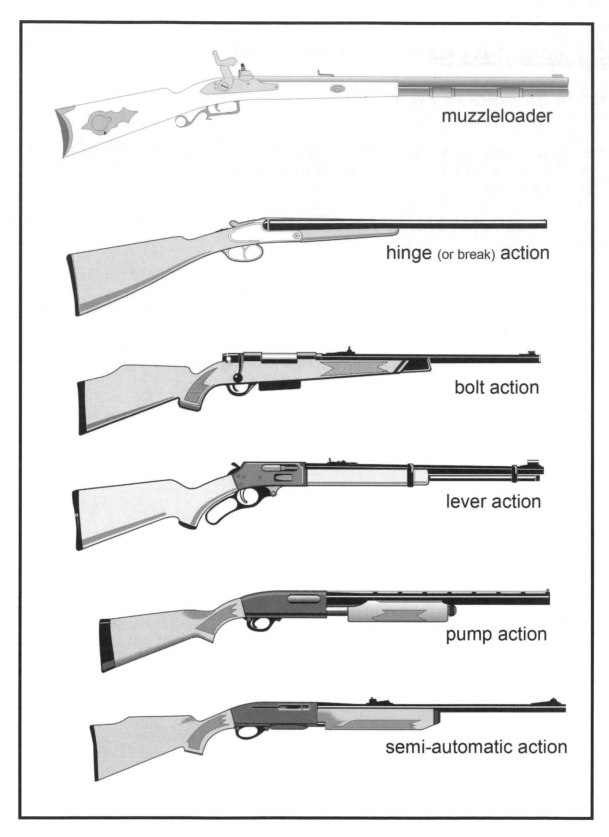

Figure 40. Types of Modern Non-restricted Firearms Actions

6.2. Safeties

6.2.0. Overview

a. A mechanical device known as a safety is included on most firearms to reduce the chances of unintentional firing. However, mechanical devices can fail. A hard blow may cause some firearms to fire even with the safety **ON**. Therefore, safe handling of a firearm by the person holding it will always be the most important firearm safety device. Always use the safety, but never rely on it to prevent firing.

b. The safety is designed to prevent the firearm from firing by interrupting the firing sequence. The safety blocks one or more of the trigger, sear, hammer or firing pin.

c. Common types of safeties on non-restricted firearms are the slide/tang, pivot/lever/rocker, wing, trigger block/lever, and cross-bolt or button safety (Figures 41 to 44). In addition, some lever action firearms and muzzleloaders use a half-cock safety.

⚠ **Never rely on a safety to prevent unintentional firing. A safety can fail. All safeties are slightly different. Consult the owner's manual. Different manufacturers may use different terminology to describe their safeties.**

6.2.1. Slide/tang safety

This safety is common on shotguns and rifles (Figure 41). It is usually on the right side of the receiver on rifles, and the top of the receiver on shotguns. It blocks the firing mechanism. Some modern lever actions also have slide- or button-type safeties located in the action area.

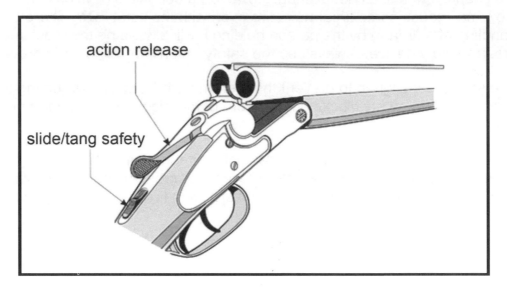

Figure 41. Side/Tang Safety

6.2.2. Pivot/lever/rocker safety

This safety is commonly found on modern firearms as well as on older military firearms (Figure 42). It is often located above the trigger area on the left or right side of the bolt.

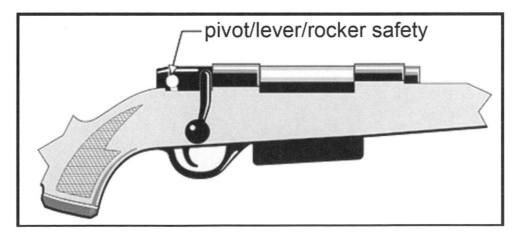

Figure 42. Pivot/Lever/Rocker Safety

103

6.2.3. Wing safety

The wing safety is frequently used on the bolt of a bolt-action firearm (Figure 43). It is often located above the trigger area on the left or right side of the bolt.

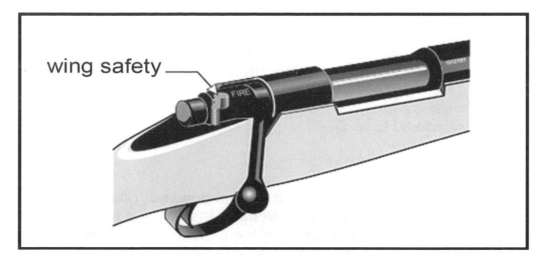

Figure 43. Wing Safety

6.2.4. Trigger block/lever safety

This safety is used on some lever action firearms (Figure 44). It is a mechanism that ensures the lever-action firearm will not fire unless the lever action is pressed firmly against the stock.

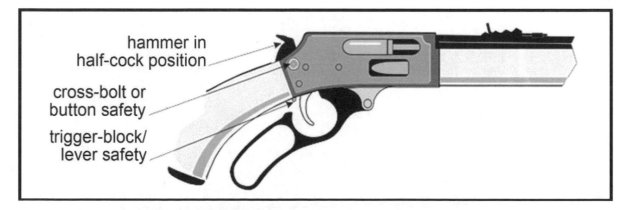

Figure 44. Trigger Block/Lever Safety

6.2.5. Hammer on half-cock notch safety

The hammer has three positions: full forward, half cock and full cock.

- When the hammer is fully forward resting on the firing pin, a sudden blow on the hammer may discharge the firearm.

- When the hammer is part-way-back or in half-cock position—on firearms so designed—the safety is considered to be **ON**.

- When the hammer is all-the-way-back on such firearms, it is in full-cock position and the safety is considered to be **OFF**.

The presence of a half cock on a firearm does not guarantee it is a safety. Some firearms do not use it as a safety. Consult the owner's manual. Remove your finger from the trigger when lowering the hammer to the half-cock position once the hammer starts to go forward. This will re-engage any automatic safety linked to the trigger. Be very careful when moving the hammer in any of the three positions as it could slip from beneath your thumb and fire the cartridge.

6.2.6. Cross-bolt safety

a. The cross-bolt safety (Figure 45) is a push-button type of safety. It is common on many types of firearms. It works by blocking the trigger mechanism or hammer.

b. The safety position can be indicated in several ways as follows:

- **safe** and **fire**;

- **ON** and **OFF** switch; or

- **red** means that the safety is **OFF**, and the firearm can be fired.

c. However, there is not one standard rule for indicating the safety position, and sometimes none of the above positions can be found on the firearm. If this is the case, ensure that the firearm is unloaded and pointing in a safe direction **BEFORE** checking the safety operation in the manufacturer's manual.

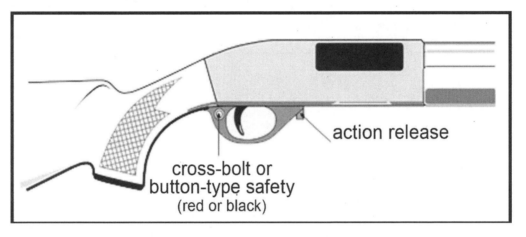

Figure 45. Cross-bolt Safety

 Before loading any firearm, determine the ON position of the safety.

6.3. Action releases

Most firearms have some type of mechanism that must be moved to allow an action to be opened or closed. The location of the action release mechanism depends on the make and model of the firearm.

⚠ **Do not touch any firearm unless you know how to handle it safely. Consult the owner's manual or a person who knows that firearm well.**

6.4. General loading and unloading procedures

6.4.0. Overview

Before attempting to unload a firearm, first follow the **Vital Four ACTS of Firearms Safety** and **PROVE it safe**.

The Vital Four ACTS of Firearm Safety	
☞	**Assume every firearm is loaded.** • Regard any firearm as a potential danger.
☞	**Control the muzzle direction at all times.** • Identify the safest available muzzle direction. • Keep the firearm pointed in the safest available direction. • The muzzle of a firearm should not be pointed towards yourself or any other person.
☞	**Trigger finger must be kept off the trigger and out of the trigger guard.** • Do **NOT** put your finger on the trigger or inside the trigger guard when you pick up a firearm.
☞	**See that the firearm is unloaded—PROVE it safe.** • Do not handle the firearm unless you can properly **PROVE it safe**. • Check to see that both chamber and magazine are empty. Do this every time you handle a firearm, for any reason. • Pass or accept only open and unloaded firearms. It is an essential rule to adopt.

6.4.1. Unloading procedure—ACTS and PROVE it safe

PROVE is an acronym, or memory aid, that stands for the five steps required to ensure that a firearm is unloaded and safe. The five steps are: **P**oint, **R**emove, **O**bserve, **V**erify and **E**xamine. These procedures must be followed to safely unload any firearm.

1. **P**oint the firearm in the safest available direction throughout the unloading procedure.

   - Make sure that nothing touches the trigger throughout this procedure.
   - Put the safety **ON**, if it can be left on during the unloading process.

2. **R**emove all ammunition as follows:

   - If the firearm has a detachable magazine, remove the magazine from the firearm first. Open the action to remove any ammunition from the chamber. (This prevents a firearm from chambering another cartridge if the action closes.)
   - Leave the action open.

3. **O**bserve the chamber(s) to confirm that there is no ammunition or empty casing(s).

4. **V**erify by inspecting the feeding path to make sure it is empty of ammunition, empty casings, or foreign objects. Make certain that you see or feel the follower, if one is present.

5. **E**xamine the bore(s) for lubricant, rust or obstructions, every time you pick up a firearm.

⚠ **The firearm is now unloaded and safe until it leaves the direct control of the person who unloaded and PROVEd it safe. Direct control is defined as having the firearm within eyesight and/or arm's reach of the shooter.**

6.4.2. Checking the barrel for obstructions

In all of the following loading procedures, always check the barrel and chamber for obstructions before loading. Whenever possible, this should be done by looking through the barrel from the BACK or breech end. If you cannot, be certain that the firearm is unloaded and the action is open and the chamber empty BEFORE looking down the barrel from the muzzle end. Some shooters prefer to use a bore light inspection aid or run a rod with a patch through the barrel before loading rather than looking down the barrel. Use normal cleaning procedures to remove an obstruction, or take the firearm to an expert.

Unless the patch fills the bore completely, obstructions may not be detected.

6.4.3. Loading procedure

Only load a firearm when you intend to use it, and only in an area where it can be safely and legally discharged.

1. Prepare the firearm for loading by going through the complete unloading procedure **ACTS—PROVE it safe**.

2. Clear any obstructions from the chamber(s) and bore(s). Clean if required.

3. Point the firearm in the safest available direction throughout the loading and chambering procedure.

4. Make sure that nothing touches the trigger throughout this process.

5. Put the safety **ON**, if it can be left on during the loading process.

6. Where possible, with the action open, select and load the correct ammunition by matching the data stamp on the firearm with the head stamp on the cartridge/shell or ammunition box.

7. Close the action.

8. Put the safety **ON**, if it is not already on.

The firearm is now loaded and ready for use. It requires continuous care and attention until it is unloaded.

⚠ **Always be sure of your target and beyond.**

6.5. Loading and unloading the most common action types

a. All firearms have their own unique aspects. One of the best ways to discover the detailed methods for unloading and loading your particular firearm is to study the owner's manual. The steps outlined in this section are not meant to replace a full understanding of a given firearm owner's manual.

b. The following information is an introduction to the most common actions. The general procedure does not change, but the details can vary significantly.

⚠ **Do not attempt to handle any firearm that you are not comfortable with. To ensure proper fit of any firearm, seek the assistance of a qualified individual. Before attempting to unload a firearm, follow The Vital Four ACTS—PROVE it safe.**

6.6. Hinge (or break) action: single or multiple barrels

The hinge (or break) action firearm (Figure 46) opens or "breaks" near the breech like the movement of a door hinge. The safety mechanism is usually located on top of the action above the trigger area. It is often a slide/tang safety or exposed hammer which must be completely down or on half cock to be safe.

6.6.1 Unloading procedure—ACTS and PROVE it safe

The Vital Four ACTS of Firearm Safety	
☞	**Assume every firearm is loaded.** • Regard any firearm as a potential danger.
☞	**Control the muzzle direction at all times.** • Identify the safest available muzzle direction. • Keep the firearm pointed in the safest available direction. • The muzzle of a firearm should not be pointed towards yourself or any other person.
☞	**Trigger finger must be kept off the trigger and out of the trigger guard.** • Do **NOT** put your finger on the trigger or inside the trigger guard when you pick up a firearm.
☞	**See that the firearm is unloaded—PROVE it safe.** • Do not handle the firearm unless you can properly **PROVE it safe**. • Check to see that both chamber and magazine are empty. Do this every time you handle a firearm, for any reason. • Pass or accept only open and unloaded firearms. It is an essential rule to adopt.

PROVE it safe

1. **P**oint the firearm in the safest available direction throughout the unloading procedure.

    - Make sure that nothing touches the trigger throughout this procedure.

    - Put the safety ON, if it can be left on during the unloading process.

2. **R**emove all ammunition as follows:

    Move the action release to open the action. If the action release will not move, the safety may need to be moved to the OFF position.

3. **O**bserve the chamber(s) to confirm that there is no ammunition or empty casing(s)/hull(s).

    - Open the action by breaking the barrel open (normally it drops downward). This should partly extract or eject any ammunition or empty casing/hull from the chambers(s). If not ejected, remove them by hand.

    - Leave the action open.

    - Ensure that all chambers are empty of casings/hulls or live ammunition.

4. **V**erify by inspecting the feeding path to make sure it is empty of ammunition, empty casing(s)/hull(s), or foreign objects.

5. **E**xamine the bore(s) for lubricant, rust or obstructions, every time you pick up a firearm.

The firearm is now unloaded and safe until it leaves the direct control of the person who unloaded and PROVEd it safe. Direct control is defined as having the firearm within eyesight and/or arm's reach of the shooter.

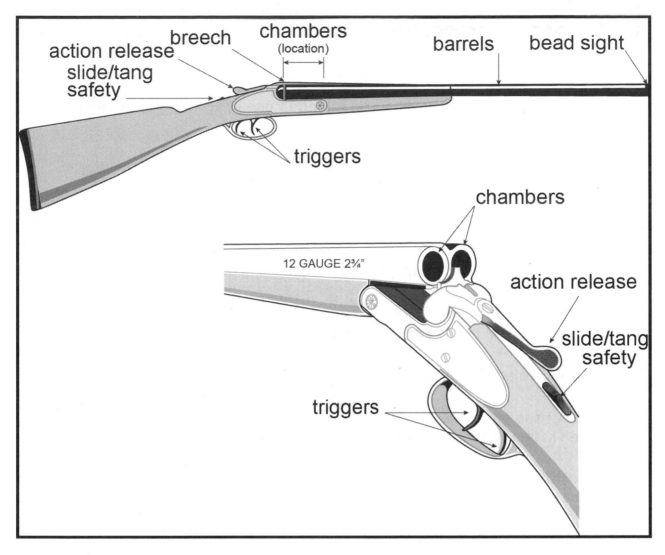

Figure 46. Hinge (or break action)

6.6.2. Loading procedure

⚠️ **Only load a firearm when you intend to use it, and only in an area where it can be safely and legally discharged.**

1. Prepare the firearm for loading by going through the complete unloading procedure—**ACTS** and **PROVE it safe**.

2. Clear any obstructions from the chamber(s) and bore(s). Clean if required.

3. Point the firearm in the safest available direction throughout the loading and chambering procedure.

4. Make sure that nothing touches the trigger throughout this process.

5. Put the safety **ON**, if it can be left on during the loading process.

6. Select and place the correct ammunition into the chamber(s) by matching the data stamp on the firearm with the head stamp on the cartridge/casing.

7. Close the action (typically by snapping it closed with a firm action), locking the cartridge(s)/shell(s) into the chamber(s).

8. Put the safety **ON**, if it is not already on.

The firearm is now loaded and ready for use. It requires continuous care and attention until it is unloaded.

⚠️ **Always be sure of your target and beyond.**

6.7. Single shot

6.7.0. Overview

a. A bolt-action firearm operates something like a door bolt. This action is very strong and is most often used on rifles.

b. The safety mechanism is usually located on top of the action above the trigger area on the left or right side of the bolt. This is often a lever safety but can also be a slide/tang located directly behind the bolt (Figures 47 and 48).

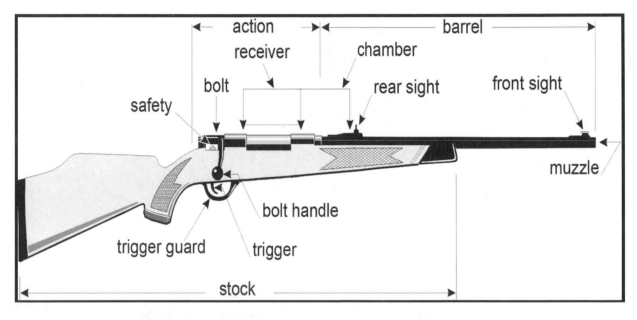

Figure 47. Bolt Action

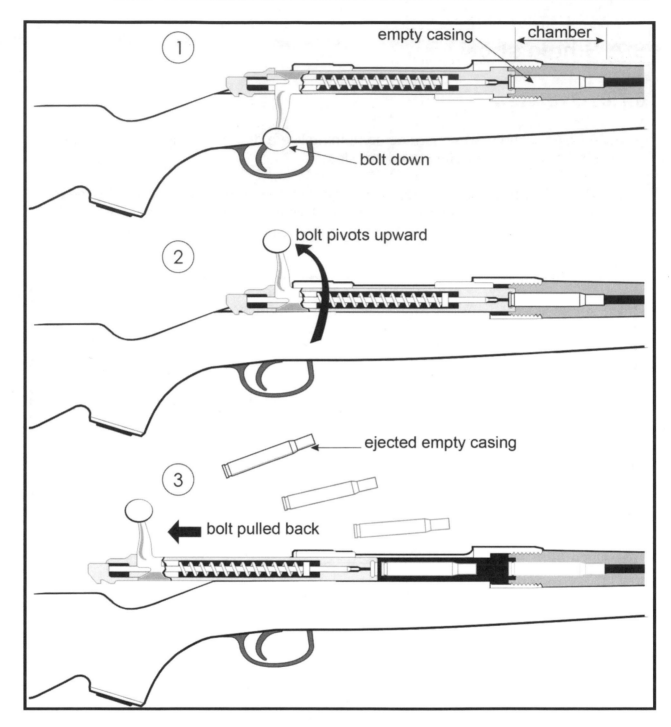

Figure 48. Single-shot Rifle Using Bolt Action to Eject Empty Casing

6.7.1. Unloading procedures: ACTS and PROVE it safe

Before attempting to unload a firearm, follow the Vital Four ACTS of Firearm Safety and PROVE it safe procedures.

	The Vital Four ACTS of Firearm Safety
☞	**Assume every firearm is loaded.** • Regard any firearm as a potential danger.
☞	**Control the muzzle direction at all times.** • Identify the safest available muzzle direction. • Keep the firearm pointed in the safest available direction. • The muzzle of a firearm should not be pointed towards yourself or any other person.
☞	**Trigger finger must be kept off the trigger and out of the trigger guard.** • Do **NOT** put your finger on the trigger or inside the trigger guard when you pick up a firearm.
☞	**See that the firearm is unloaded—PROVE it safe.** • Do not handle the firearm unless you can properly **PROVE it safe**. • Check to see that both chamber and magazine are empty. Do this every time you handle a firearm, for any reason. • Pass or accept only open and unloaded firearms. It is an essential rule to adopt.

PROVE it safe

1. **P**oint the firearm in the safest available direction throughout the unloading procedure.

   - Make sure that nothing touches the trigger throughout this procedure.

   - Put the safety ON, if it can be left on during the unloading process.

2. **R**emove all ammunition as follows:

   - Open the action by moving the bolt handle (typically by lifting and pulling to the rear). This should extract and eject any ammunition or empty the casing/hull from the chamber. If not ejected, remove it by hand.

   - Leave the action open.

3. **O**bserve the chamber to confirm that there is no ammunition or empty casing/hull.

4. **V**erify by inspecting the feeding path to make sure it is empty of ammunition, empty casings/hulls, or foreign objects.

5. **E**xamine the bore(s) for lubricant, rust or obstructions, every time you pick up a firearm.

Only load a firearm when you intend to use it, and only in an area where it can be safely and legally discharged.

⚠ The firearm is now unloaded and safe until it leaves the direct control of the person who unloaded and PROVEd it safe. Direct control is defined as having the firearm within eyesight and/or arm's reach of the shooter.

6.7.2. Loading procedure

⚠ **Only load a firearm when you intend to use it, and only in an area where it can be safely and legally discharged**.

1. Prepare the firearm for loading by going through the complete unloading procedure, **ACTS** and **PROVE it safe**.

2. Select and place the correct ammunition into the magazine by matching the data stamp on the firearm with the head stamp on the cartridge or ammunition box.

3. Put the safety **ON**, if it can be left on during the loading process.

4. Close the actions by moving the bolt handle forward and down, locking the cartridge into the chamber.

5. Put the safety **ON**, it if is not already on.

The firearm is now loaded and ready for use. It requires continuous care and attention until it is unloaded.

⚠ **Always be sure of your target and beyond.**

6.8. Operating repeating firearms

6.8.0. Overview

a. Many firearms are repeaters. Although they have only one chamber, they can be fired several times in a row because they hold more than one cartridge or shell. Some kind of hand movement must be made by the shooter to load another cartridge into the firing position.

The most common repeating firearms include the following:

- bolt action;

- lever action;

- pump action; and

- semi-automatic action.

b. The extra ammunition in a repeating firearm is usually contained in some kind of magazine. Magazines are located in different places depending on the make, model and action of the firearm. There are two common types of magazines:

- box; and

- tubular.

6.8.1. Box magazine

The usual location of a **box magazine** is shown in Figure 49. Some box magazines may be removed by depressing a button or latch. Some are not removable.

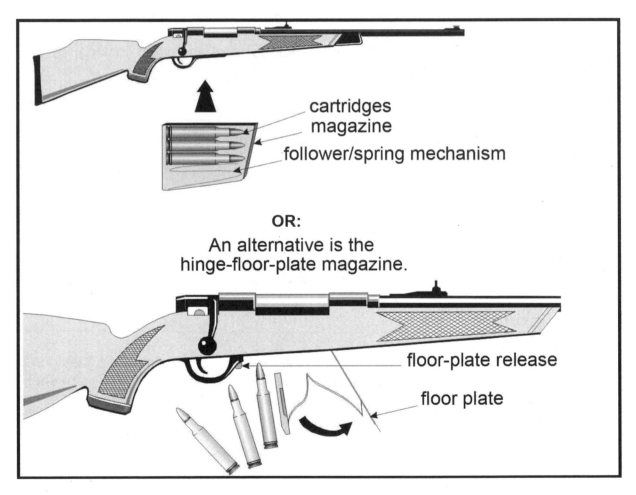

Figure 49. Box-type Magazine

6.8.2. Tubular magazine

a. The tubular magazine is usually found in one of two locations:

- under the barrel; or

- in the stock.

b. Many tubular magazines consist of a removable inner magazine tube (which should be removed when unloading the firearm).

c. To unload tubular magazines, remove the inside tube and let the ammunition drop out of the end of the fixed-tubular magazine or the loading port. If the inner tube is not removable, close and open the action several times to be sure that there is no ammunition in the magazine. Take extra care in performing this procedure because when doing so, the firearm is in the ready-to-fire position.

 Ammunition could hang-up in the tubular magazine, due to dirt, rust or dents. Always be sure you can feel or see the magazine follower to confirm that all the ammunition is out.

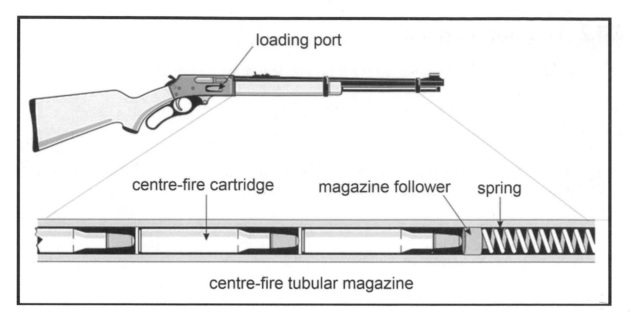

Figure 50. Tubular-type Magazine (centre-fire)

> ⚠ **In most cases, using pointed centre-fire ammunition in a tubular magazine is hazardous. If jarred, the point on one of the cartridges may detonate the primer of the one in front of it. Check with ammunition manufacturers for compatibility.**

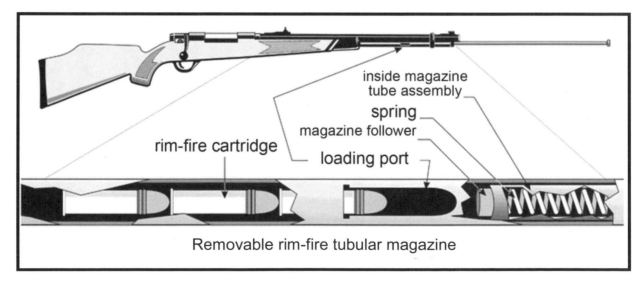

Figure 51. Tubular-type Magazine (rim-fire)

> **Magazine Capacity Limits**
>
> **Part 4** of the *Regulations Prescribing Certain Firearms and other Weapons, Components, and Parts of Weapons, Accessories, Cartridge Magazines, Ammunition and Projectiles as Prohibited or Restricted*, sets out the limits for the number of cartridges permitted for different types of magazines.
>
> For example, centre-fire semi-automatic rifles and shotguns including "grandfathered" full-automatics and converted full-automatics— 5-shot magazines.

These restrictions do not apply to rim-fire rifles in general, M-1 Garand rifles and other rare historically valuable magazines that have been specifically exempt, as well as non semi-automatic rifles (pump, lever or bolt action). Prior to July 1993, owners of large-capacity cartridge magazines that were affected by the limits were able to retain them if they had been properly modified to comply with the limits.

6.9. Bolt-action repeaters

6.9.0. Overview

a. Federal, provincial and territorial laws may affect the number of cartridges you are allowed to have in a magazine while hunting. Consult your course instructor or your provincial/territorial hunting authority.

b. A bolt-action firearm operates in a similar way to a door bolt. This action is very strong and is most often used on rifles.

c. The safety mechanism is usually located on top of the action above the trigger area on the left or right side of the bolt. This is often a lever-type safety but can also be a slide/tang located directly behind the bolt (Figure 52).

 Never rely on the firearm's safety. Safeties can wear down and may not work properly. Also, a loaded firearm may fire even with the safety on. All mechanical devices can fail.

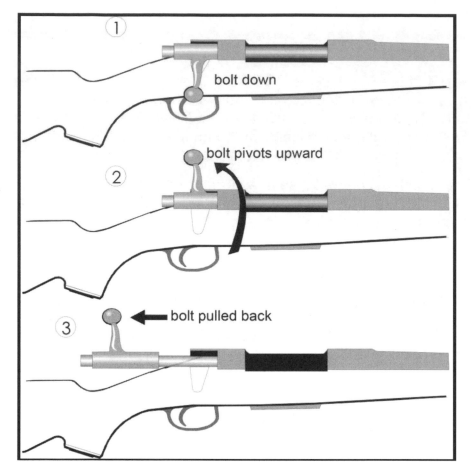

Figure 52. Bolt-action Repeater

6.9.1. Unloading procedure: ACTS and PROVE it safe

Before attempting to unload a firearm, follow the Vital Four ACTS of Firearm Safety and PROVE it safe.

The Vital Four ACTS of Firearm Safety

Assume every firearm is loaded.

- Regard any firearm as a potential danger.

Control the muzzle direction at all times.

- Identify the safest available muzzle direction.
- Keep the firearm pointed in the safest available direction.
- The muzzle of a firearm should not be pointed towards yourself or any other person.

Trigger finger must be kept off the trigger and out of the trigger guard.

- Do **NOT** put your finger on the trigger or inside the trigger guard when you pick up a firearm.

See that the firearm is unloaded—PROVE it safe.

- Do not handle the firearm unless you can properly **PROVE it safe**.
- Check to see that both chamber and magazine are empty. Do this every time you handle a firearm, for any reason.
- Pass or accept only open and unloaded firearms. It is an essential rule to adopt.

PROVE it safe

1. **P**oint the firearm in the safest available direction throughout the unloading procedure.

   - Make sure that nothing touches the trigger throughout this procedure.

   - Put the safety **ON**, if it can be left on during the unloading process.

2. **R**emove all ammunition as follows:

   - Open the action by moving the bolt handle (typically up and to the rear). This should extract and eject any ammunition or empty casing/hull from the chamber. If not ejected, remove it by hand.

   - If the magazine (inner tube or box) is removable, remove the magazine.

   - Remove any ammunition using gravity to make it fall out (typically from the front of the open end of the tubular magazine).

   - If the ammunition cannot be removed in any other way, cycle all the cartridges through the chamber to get them out.

   - Leave the action open.

3. **O**bserve the chamber to confirm that there is no ammunition or empty casings/hulls.

4. **V**erify by inspecting the feeding path to make sure it is empty of ammunition, empty casings/hulls, or foreign objects. Make certain that you see or feel the follower, if one is present.

5. **EX**amine the bore(s) for lubricant, rust or obstructions, every time you pick up a firearm.

⚠ **The firearm is now unloaded and safe until it leaves the direct control of the person who unloaded and PROVEd it safe. Direct control is defined as having the firearm within eyesight and/or arm's reach of the shooter.**

6.9.2. Loading procedure

⚠ **Only load a firearm when you intend to use it, and only in an area where it can be safely and legally discharged**.

1. Prepare the firearm for loading by going through the complete unloading procedure—**ACTS and PROVE it safe**.

2. Select and place the correct ammunition into the magazine by matching the data stamp on the firearm with the head stamp on the cartridge or the ammunition box.

3. Put the safety **ON**, if it can be left on during the loading process.

4. On some firearms, you must release the spring tension on the follower at this point.

5. Re-apply spring tension to the follower or insert the magazine, if necessary.

6. Close the action by moving the bolt handle (typically forward and downward), feeding and locking a cartridge into the chamber.

7. Put the safety **ON**, if it is not already on.

The firearm is now loaded and ready for use. It requires continuous care and attention until it is loaded.

⚠ **Always be sure of your target and beyond.**

6.10. Lever-action repeaters

6.10.0. Overview

a. A lever-action firearm has a metal handle located just behind the trigger (Figure 53). This action is most often used on rifles.

b. In most cases, the safety mechanism is an exposed hammer. The hammer has three positions—forward, half cock and full cock. When the hammer is in half-cock position, the safety is considered to be **ON**. When the hammer is all-the-way-back, it is in full-cock position and the safety is considered to be **OFF**. However, when the hammer is fully forward resting on the firing pin, a sudden blow on the hammer can discharge the firearm.

c. This type of lever action often will not fire unless the lever is fully squeezed against the stock depressing the trigger-block safety.

d. Some modern lever-action firearms also have slide/tang or cross-bolt/button safeties located in the action area.

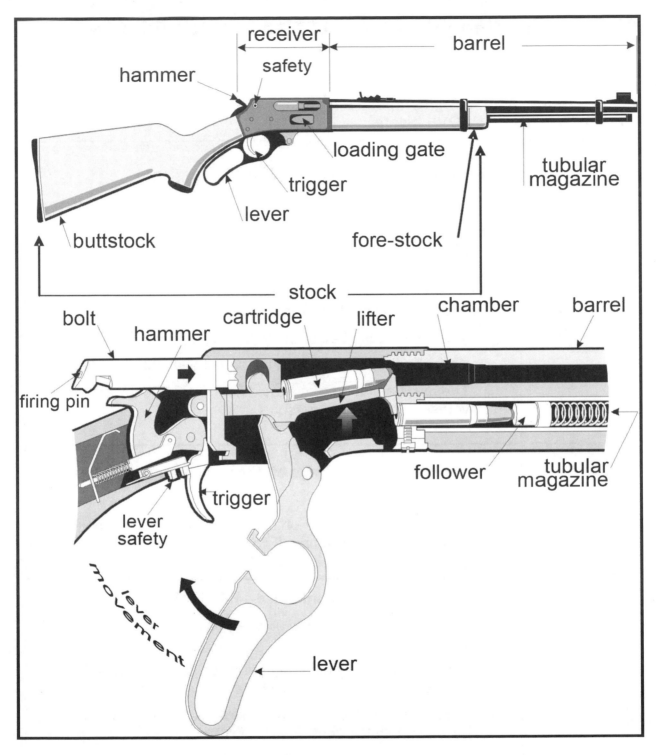

Figure 53. Lever Action

6.10.1. Unloading procedure: ACTS and PROVE it safe

⚠ Before attempting to unload a firearm, follow the Vital Four ACTS of Firearm Safety, and PROVE it safe.

The Vital Four ACTS of Firearm Safety
Assume every firearm is loaded. • Regard any firearm as a potential danger.
Control the muzzle direction at all times. • Identify the safest available muzzle direction. • Keep the firearm pointed in the safest available direction. • The muzzle of a firearm should not be pointed towards yourself or any other person.
Trigger finger must be kept off the trigger and out of the trigger guard. • Do **NOT** put your finger on the trigger or inside the trigger guard when you pick up a firearm.
See that the firearm is unloaded—PROVE it safe. • Do not handle the firearm unless you can properly **PROVE it safe**. • Check to see that both chamber and magazine are empty. Do this every time you handle a firearm, for any reason. • Pass or accept only open and unloaded firearms. It is an essential rule to adopt.

PROVE it safe

1. **P**oint the firearm in the safest available direction throughout the unloading procedure.

   - Make sure that nothing touches the trigger throughout this procedure.
   - Put the safety **ON**, if it can be left on during the unloading process.

2. **R**emove all cartridges as follows:

   - Open the action by moving the lever downward. This should extract and eject any cartridge or empty casing from the chamber.
   - If the magazine (inner tubular or box) is removable, remove the magazine.
   - If it cannot be removed, and if spring tension to the follower can be released, release it.
   - If applicable, remove any cartridges using gravity to make them fall out (typically from the front of the open end of the box or inner-tubular magazine or, when not removable, from the loading port), then
   - Re-apply spring tension to the follower, if not, cycle the action repeatedly until the feeding path is clear (close and re-open it).
   - Leave the action open.

3. **O**bserve the chamber(s) to confirm that there is no cartridge or empty casings/hulls.

4. **V**erify by inspecting the feeding path to make sure it is empty of cartridges, empty casings/hulls or foreign objects. Make certain that you see or feel the follower, if one is present.

5. **E**xamine the bore(s) for lubricant, rust or obstructions, every time you pick up a firearm.

⚠ **The firearm is now unloaded and safe until it leaves the direct control of the person who unloaded and PROVEd it safe. Direct control is defined as having the firearm within eyesight and/or arm's reach of the shooter.**

6.10.2. Loading procedure

 Only load a firearm when you intend to use it, and only in an area where it can be safely and legally discharged.

1. Prepare the firearm for loading by going through the complete unloading procedure, **ACTS and PROVE it safe**.

2. Select and place the correct ammunition into the magazine by matching the data stamp on the firearm with the head stamp on the cartridge or the ammunition box.

3. Put the safety **ON**, if it can be left on during the loading process.

4. Close the action by moving the lever, feeding and locking a cartridge into the chamber.

5. Put the safety **ON**, if it is not already on.

The firearm is now loaded and ready for use. It requires continuous care and attention until it is unloaded.

Always be sure of your target and beyond.

6.11. Pump-action repeaters

6.11.0. Overview

a. The pump-action firearm is sometimes called the slide or trombone action because the fore-end of the stock is pumped back and forth to operate the action. It permits rapid reloading with a simple movement of the firearm-supporting hand without moving the muzzle away from the target. This action is most commonly used on shotguns. Either a box or a tubular magazine may be used.

b. The **safety mechanism** on most modern pump actions is either a slide/tang or cross-bolt/button safety located in the action area. The button is usually at the front or rear of the trigger guard. The slide/tang is frequently on top of the action. The action release is also found at the trigger guard (Figure 54).

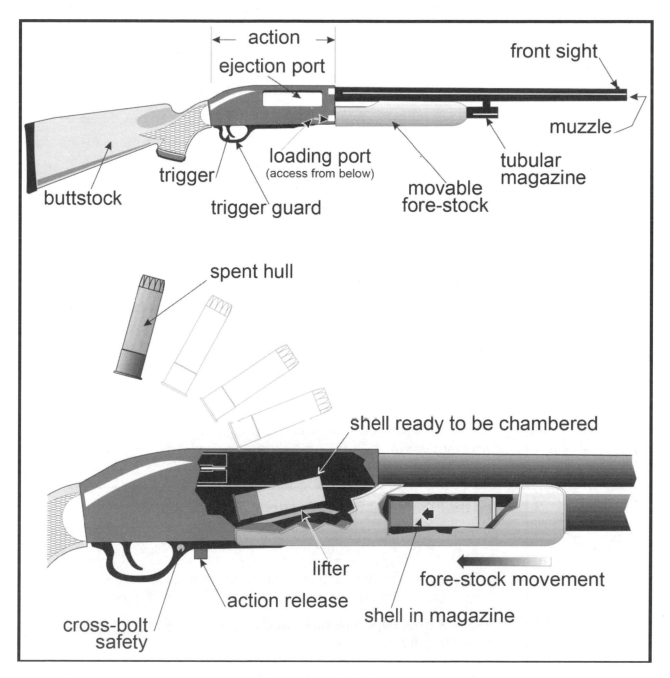

Figure 54. Pump Action

6.11.1. Unloading procedure: ACTS and PROVE it safe

Before attempting to unload a firearm, follow the Vital Four ACTS of Firearm Safety and PROVE it safe.

The Vital Four ACTS of Firearm Safety	
☞	**Assume every firearm is loaded.** • Regard any firearm as a potential danger.
☞	**Control the muzzle direction at all times.** • Identify the safest available muzzle direction. • Keep the firearm pointed in the safest available direction. • The muzzle of a firearm should not be pointed towards yourself or any other person.
☞	**Trigger finger must be kept off the trigger and out of the trigger guard.** • Do **NOT** put your finger on the trigger or inside the trigger guard when you pick up a firearm.
☞	**See that the firearm is unloaded—PROVE it safe.** • Do not handle the firearm unless you can properly **PROVE it safe**. • Check to see that both chamber and magazine are empty. Do this every time you handle a firearm, for any reason. • Pass or accept only open and unloaded firearms. It is an essential rule to adopt.

PROVE it safe

1. **P**oint the firearm in the safest available direction throughout the unloading procedure.

   - Make sure that nothing touches the trigger throughout this procedure.

   - Put the safety **ON**, if it can be left on during the unloading process.

2. **R**emove all ammunition as follows:

   - Open the action by depressing the action release and sliding the fore-stock to the rear. This should extract and eject any ammunition or empty casing/hull from the chamber. If not ejected, remove it by hand.

   - If the magazine is removable, remove the magazine. Remove any ammunition using gravity to make it fall out (typically from the front of the open end of the tubular magazine).

   - If ammunition cannot be removed in any other way, cycle all the cartridges through the chamber to get them out.

   - Leave the action open.

3. **O**bserve the chamber(s) to confirm that there is no ammunition or empty casings/hulls.

4. **V**erify by inspecting the feeding path to make sure it is empty of ammunition, empty casings/hulls or foreign objects. Make certain that you see or feel the follower, if one is present.

5. **E**xamine the bore(s) for lubricant, rust or obstructions, every time you pick up a firearm.

⚠ **The firearm is now unloaded and safe until it leaves the direct control of the person who unloaded and PROVEd it safe. Direct control is defined as having the firearm within eyesight and/or arm's reach of the shooter.**

6.11.2. Loading procedure

⚠️ **Only load a firearm when you intend to use it, and only in an area where it can be safely and legally discharged.**

1. Prepare the firearm for loading by going through the complete unloading procedure: **ACTS and PROVE it safe**.

2. Select and place the correct ammunition into the magazine by matching the data stamp on the firearm with the head stamp on the cartridge or ammunition box.

3. Put the safety **ON**, if it can be left on during the loading process.

4. Move the fore-stock to the forward position to close the action.

5. Cycle the action moving a cartridge from the magazine into the chamber.

6. Put the safety **ON**, if it is not already on.

The firearm is now loaded and ready for use. It requires continuous care and attention until it is unloaded.

⚠️ **Always be sure of your target and beyond.**

6.12. Semi-automatic action repeaters

6.12.0. Overview

a. This action can be found on rifles and shotguns.

b. With each pull of the trigger, the semi-automatic action uses part of the energy of the expanding gas from the burning powder to extract the empty cartridge case and to reload the chamber. In other words, no hand movement is needed to load another cartridge into the firing position; each time a cartridge is fired, another is loaded into the chamber (Figure 55).

c. Semi-automatic safeties vary considerably. The safety mechanisms commonly used are cross-bolt/button and slide/tang types. Occasionally, internal safeties such as a magazine disconnect are used. These prevent the firearm from firing when the magazine is not in place.

Magazine Capacity Limits

Part 4 of the *Regulations Prescribing Certain Firearms and other Weapons, Components, and Parts of Weapons, Accessories, Cartridge Magazines, Ammunition and Projectiles as Prohibited or Restricted*, sets out the limits for the number of cartridges permitted for different types of magazines.

For example, centre-fire semi-automatic rifles and shotguns, including "grandfathered," full-automatics and converted full-automatics, have 5-shot magazines.

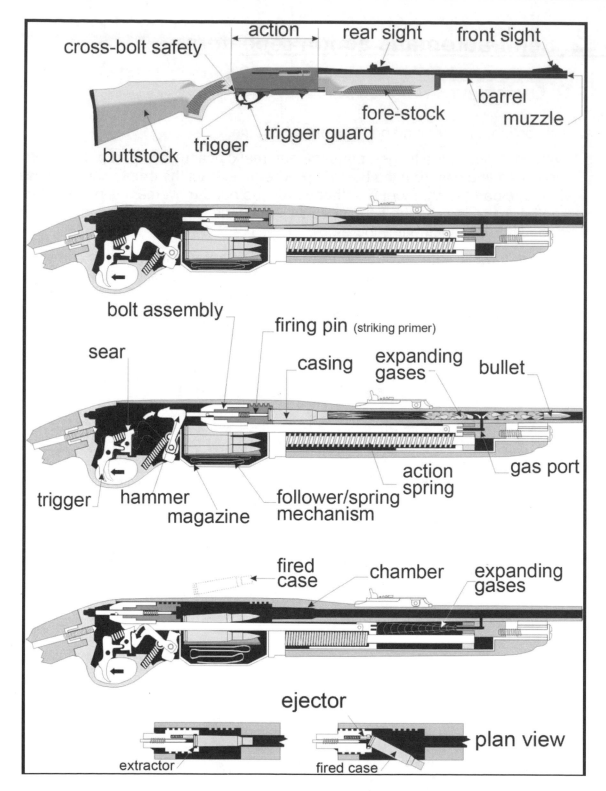

Figure 55. Firing Sequence of a Semi-automatic Rifle

6.12.1. Unloading procedure: ACTS and PROVE it safe

⚠ **Before attempting to unload a firearm, follow the Vital Four ACTS of Firearm Safety, and PROVE it safe.**

The Vital Four ACTS of Firearm Safety
Assume every firearm is loaded. • Regard any firearm as a potential danger.
Control the muzzle direction at all times. • Identify the safest available muzzle direction. • Keep the firearm pointed in the safest available direction. • The muzzle of a firearm should not be pointed towards yourself or any other person.
Trigger finger must be kept off the trigger and out of the trigger guard. • Do **NOT** put your finger on the trigger or inside the trigger guard when you pick up a firearm.
See that the firearm is unloaded—PROVE it safe. • Do not handle the firearm unless you can properly **PROVE it safe**. • Check to see that both chamber and magazine are empty. Do this every time you handle a firearm, for any reason. • Pass or accept only open and unloaded firearms. It is an essential rule to adopt.

PROVE it safe

1. **P**oint the firearm in the safest available direction throughout the unloading procedure.

   - Make sure that nothing touches the trigger throughout this procedure.

   - Put the safety **ON**, if it can be left on during the unloading process.

2. **R**emove all ammunition as follows:

   - If the magazine (inner tubular or box) is removable, remove the magazine. If applicable, remove any cartridges using gravity to make them fall out (typically from the front of the open end of the tubular magazine).

   - If the ammunition cannot be removed in any other way, cycle all the ammunition through the chamber to get them out.

   - Open the action by operating the cocking device (slide or bolt). This should extract and eject any ammunition or empty casing/hull from the chamber.

3. **O**bserve the chamber(s) to confirm that there is no ammunition or empty casings/hulls.

4. **V**erify by inspecting the feeding path to make sure it is empty of ammunition, empty casings/hulls or foreign objects. Make certain that you see or feel the follower, if one is present.

5. **E**xamine the bore(s) for lubricant, rust or obstructions, every time you pick up a firearm.

⚠ The firearm is now unloaded and safe until it leaves the direct control of the person who unloaded and PROVEd it safe. Direct control is defined as having the firearm within eyesight and/or arm's reach of the shooter.

6.12.2. Loading procedure

⚠️ **Only load a firearm when you intend to use it, and only in an area where it can be safely and legally discharged.**

1. Prepare the firearm for loading by going through the complete unloading procedure, **ACTS and PROVE it safe**.

2. Select and place the correct ammunition into the magazine by matching the data stamp on the firearm with the head stamp on the cartridge.

3. Put the safety **ON**, if it can be left on during the loading process.

4. Replace the magazine.

5. Close the action by operating the action release, locking ammunition into the chamber.

6. Put the safety **ON**, if it is not already on.

The firearm is now loaded and ready for use. It requires continuous care and attention until it is unloaded.

⚠️ **Always be sure of your target and beyond.**

6.13. Firearm malfunctions

⚠️ **Generally, when using commercially made ammunition and a properly maintained firearm, malfunctions will not occur. Firearms jammed with a cartridge or shell in the chamber(s) can be a hazard. This hazard, if not dealt with properly, may result in a serious incident. Consult a qualified person or gunsmith for information on how to perform this function in the safest possible manner with your particular firearm.**

6.14. Review questions

1. Name the safety that is located on top of the receiver, which is operated by sliding it forward or backward with your thumb.

2. Name the safety where the hammer is pulled back to the first click, away from the firing pin.

3. When operating a cross-bolt safety, what indicates that the gun is ready to fire? Describe this position.

4. Name the safety which is released when the lever action is pulled tight against the stock allowing the gun to shoot.

5. Write out in full the expansion of the following two acronyms:

   A –

   C –

   T –

   S –

   P –

   R –

   O –

   V –

   E –

MODULE 7:

SAFE HANDLING AND CARRYING OF NON-RESTRICTED FIREARMS

MODULE 7: SAFE HANDLING AND CARRYING OF NON-RESTRICTED FIREARMS

7.0. Overview

This section looks at personal safety protection and shows you how to safely handle non-restricted firearms in the following situations:

- entering or leaving vehicles;

- shooting at a firing range;

- outdoors; and

- shooting or hunting with a group.

⚠️ **Only load a firearm when you intend to use it, and only in an area where it can be safely and legally discharged. A safe practice is not to chamber a cartridge until ready to fire.**

7.1. Range commands

The following are examples of typical range commands:

- "The range is active".

- "Cease-fire".

- "The range is no longer active".

⚠️ **Range commands and signals vary between shooting sports, ranges and jurisdictions. Be sure you are aware of and clearly understand the commands used in your area. If you are unsure, ask the Range Officer (RO) or a local official before you go to the range (Appendix G: Visual Range Signals and Devices).**

7.2. Personal safety protection

7.2.0. Overview

Like many active sports, shooting has the potential to cause personal injury. The careful shooter takes steps to avoid these injuries by wearing personal safety protection.

7.2.1. Sight protection

a. There is a risk of eye injury in shooting. Shooters going through thick brush can be injured by twigs and branches. Target shooters also risk eye injury. This can come from ejected cartridge casings. It can also come from cartridge casing fragments and other debris ejected during firing.

b. To avoid these hazards, shooters should wear safety glasses made of impact-resistant glass or polycarbonate plastic with side shields (Figure 56). They also guard against firearm malfunctions, stray shotgun pellets or bullet fragments.

Figure 56. Sight and Hearing Protection

7.2.2. Hearing protection

a. Continued unprotected exposure to shooting noise will cause hearing loss. The noise level of a gunshot is similar to that of a jet engine taking off at close range. The need for hearing protection is obvious.

b. Several types of hearing protection are available. On the firing range, shooters should always wear headphone-type hearing protectors (Figure 56). These protectors provide reasonable sound protection. They can also be used for years with minimum maintenance.

c. Earplugs are available in several types. Disposable earplugs are made of foam or wax, but they can only be used once.

d. There are also reusable earplugs made of rubber available in several sizes. They require care and cleaning after use.

e. For maximum hearing protection, it is highly recommended that both earplugs and headphone-type hearing protectors be worn.

7.2.3. Slips and falls

a. The risk of slips and falls may occur when handling firearms. This can best be avoided by using common sense.

b. If you do fall, remember your first action should be to control the muzzle of the firearm.

c. In the field, pick out the safest trail. Do not depend on surrounding branches to support your weight. Do not cross streams on wet logs or wobbly stones with a loaded firearm.

d. Wearing deep tread high boots will reduce the possibility of slips. They will also protect your ankles and legs from cuts and scrapes.

e. It is recommended that you wear blaze orange when hunting. Some provinces require this by law.

f. Beware of cumbersome clothing like bulky jackets or wading boots. They can cause you to get tangled. They can also interfere with the safe handling of your firearm.

 Occasionally, a hot, ejected cartridge casing may come in contact with unprotected skin. This can cause a shooter to flinch. The sudden movement could result in unsafe muzzle control or unintentional discharge. Therefore, button up the collar and sleeves of your shirt or blouse. This way, a hot cartridge casing cannot get inside.

7.3. Safety procedures on an approved range

Every range has rules of safe behaviour. These may vary but will normally include the standard ones shown below:

- The muzzle must always be pointed down range.

- The action of any firearm must be open at all times, except when actually shooting.

- Firearms must only be loaded, unloaded and discharged at the firing line.

- No firearm is loaded until the command to load is given by the RO.

- Fingers must be kept out of the trigger guard and off the trigger until the firearm is pointed down range.

- Upon the command "cease-fire," all firing stops at once. Firearms are unloaded. Actions are opened. Firearms are laid on the mat or on the table. Their muzzles point in a safe direction down range. The shooter steps back from the firing line, behind the "cease-fire" line.

- The RO will inspect each firearm before allowing anyone to go forward of the firing line.

- During a "cease-fire," no one will handle firearms or ammunition or return to the firing line. At this point, wait for further range commands before any further activity. Persons not engaged in changing targets down range should stand well behind the cease-fire line.

- Use hearing and sight protection.

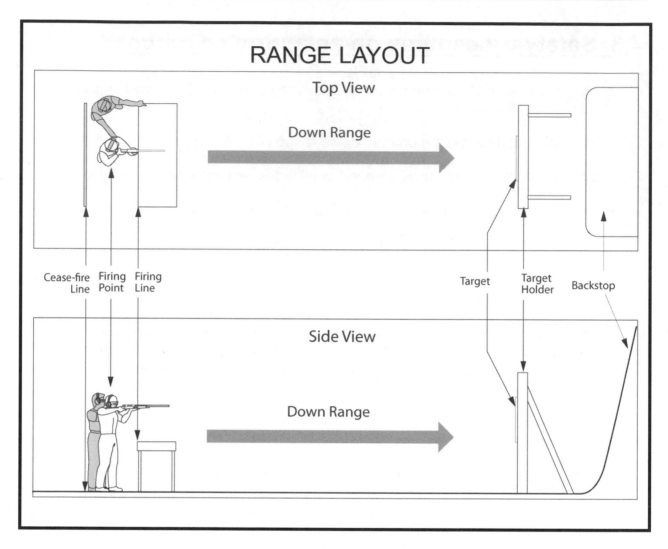

Figure 57. Range Layout with Direct Supervision

7.3.1. Additional range safety suggestions

⚠ In an emergency, <u>anyone</u> can call a "cease-fire."

There are other rules we recommend you follow:

- Minors and guests, who do not have a valid firearms licence, must be under direct and immediate supervision while shooting. Check with your range for any further restrictions.

- Firearms should be checked by the RO on the "cease-fire." This is to be sure that all actions are opened and no cartridges are in the breech.

- Unloaded firearms not in use are to be placed in the designated area with the action open or kept in a case. They should be moved with the muzzle pointed in the safest available direction or cased at the firing line.

- Never allow horseplay, careless handling of firearms or any other distraction while shooting is in progress.

- Make sure that you are using the correct ammunition for your firearm, and as approved by the range.

- Never shoot at target holders or other range equipment.

- Do not discharge firearms outside of designated range property or posted range use times.

> Direct and immediate supervision is defined as the supervisor being within arm's reach of the shooter at all times when shooting activity is being supervised.

⚠ Where shooting activities are regularly scheduled, the CFO for a province or territory must issue an approval under the authority of the *Firearms Act*. Such ranges are subject to rules and procedures that may differ from province to province. Check with your local authorities.

7.4. Range courtesy

There are certain standards of range courtesy. Rules and procedures vary between ranges. Check and obey local rules. Some of these standards are listed below:

- There should be a safety briefing before starting.

- Sign in to the firing range upon arrival, if required.

- Avoid interrupting or distracting others when they are shooting.

- Do not smoke on the firing line.

- Ask the owner's or shooter's permission before handling that person's firearms or equipment.

- Leave enough space between you and others to ensure safety.

- If firing particularly smoky firearms, shoot from downwind of other shooters on the firing line. Black-powder firearms are especially smoky.

- Do not fire on other people's targets, targets not directly down range from yourself or any target that may disturb others.

- Those firing semi-automatic firearms should take a firing point where other people will not be disturbed by ejected casings.

- Rapid firing may disturb shooters sighting-in or doing deliberate target work.

- When the line is clear, clean up after shooting, pick up cartridge casings and take down targets.

- Put away any range-owned equipment you have used, i.e., sandbags or bench rests.

7.5. Safe handling of firearms in vehicles

a. The word **vehicle** may include boats, cars, recreational vehicles, snowmobiles, sleds, private aircraft, and/or all-terrain vehicles, depending on your particular jurisdiction.

b. When handling firearms around any type of vehicle, follow the steps below:

1. **Never have a loaded firearm in or on any vehicle unless you are allowed to shoot from that vehicle.** Unload before entry. Load only after leaving.

2. It is especially difficult to control muzzle direction when entering or leaving vehicles. Take extra care to point the muzzle in the safest available direction at such times.

3. When a firearm is in a vehicle, it must be placed in a secure position where it will not be dislodged or stepped upon.

⚠️ **Check with provincial or territorial authorities in your area. They can inform you of how the transportation of firearms is regulated locally.**

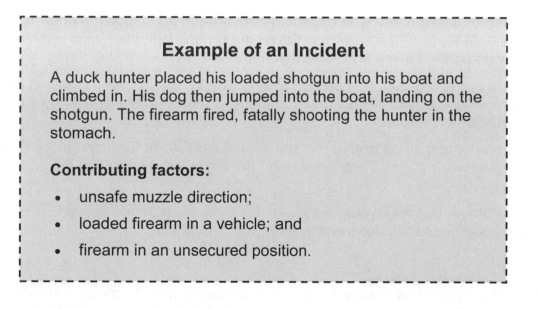

Example of an Incident

A duck hunter placed his loaded shotgun into his boat and climbed in. His dog then jumped into the boat, landing on the shotgun. The firearm fired, fatally shooting the hunter in the stomach.

Contributing factors:

- unsafe muzzle direction;
- loaded firearm in a vehicle; and
- firearm in an unsecured position.

7.6. Safe handling of firearms outdoors

a. Always remember that people or livestock you cannot see may be close enough to be injured. Be aware of the dangerous range of your firearm and ammunition.

b. Control the muzzle direction at all times. Keep the safety ON until you are ready to use the firearm.

c. Under all circumstances, protect the trigger and safety while carrying your firearm. A twig or branch may catch the trigger, put the safety off, or swing the muzzle around.

d. When carrying a firearm, remember that you can slip and fall causing a discharge. Plan how to protect the firearm and control its direction if you fall, and if possible, unload it before crossing uneven ground or ice.

e. Always be sure of your target and beyond. Don't shoot at game near the top of a hill. People or livestock may be in the line of fire over the hill. Never shoot near a building without permission. Someone may be using it as a shelter.

f. Water, rocks or flat surfaces may cause the bullet to break up or ricochet. Use caution.

g. When you cross a fence or other obstacle, unload your firearm and leave the action open. The same goes for areas that are slippery, rocky or uneven.

h. When crossing a fence alone, unload the firearm and place the firearm under the fence. Make sure the firearm is flat on the ground with the action open and the muzzle pointed away from where you are crossing.

i. If you are in a group, one person should stand away from the crossing point. This person should hold the unloaded and open firearms while the others cross the obstacle.

j. When hunting alone from a pit or blind, unload your firearm and place it outside before entering. Then enter and bring the unloaded firearm into the pit or blind after you.

k. Remember to check your firearm for dirt if you lay it on the ground. This is especially important for the muzzle.

⚠ **Use binoculars if you need to see something more clearly. Never use a scope mounted on a firearm as a substitute for binoculars to identify persons, animals or objects.**

Figure 58. Individual Crossing a Fence Safely

Figure 59. Group Crossing a Fence Safely

7.7. Shooting or hunting with a group

7.7.0 Overview

Any shot fired in the wrong direction might hit another person in your group. Make sure safe zones of fire are established to prevent such incidents. It is very important to follow the safety rules in this Handbook. The rules below are especially important for shooting or hunting with a group.

7.7.1. Informal firing line

An informal firing line is an effective method to use when sighting-in or shooting in a field, with a group of two or more people. Follow these basic safety steps below:

1. Appoint someone as the RO. This person will be responsible for supervising all of the following steps.

2. Follow the normal range commands and procedures.

3. Set up a firing line. Firearms may only be uncased, handled and loaded at this firing line. This must be done under the RO's direction.

4. Be sure that the appointed RO explains the procedures to everyone in the group.

5. Decide on a safe shooting zone for each shooter. Make sure there is a safe backstop. This will be the only direction in which muzzles can be pointed and firearms fired.

7.7.2. Safe zones of fire

a. It is worth emphasizing again. Any shot fired in the wrong direction by a group member might hit another person. This is true for all shooting situations. Before starting, everybody should agree on which area each shooter will cover in order to prevent this (Figure 60). This will clearly define each individual's safe zone of fire.

b. Positions change when you advance through the field. You should always know exactly where your shooting partners are. Guard both them and yourself against being unintentionally shot.

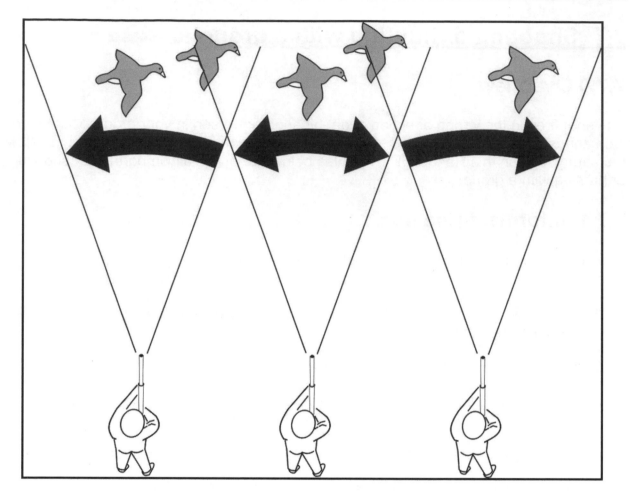

Figure 60. Safe Zones of Fire

⚠️ **Always know exactly where your shooting partners, or others, are.**

7.8. Carrying positions

Muzzle direction is all-important when carrying firearms. You can control muzzle direction safely if you use proper carrying positions. When carrying firearms, you must always be aware of the possibility of slips or falls.

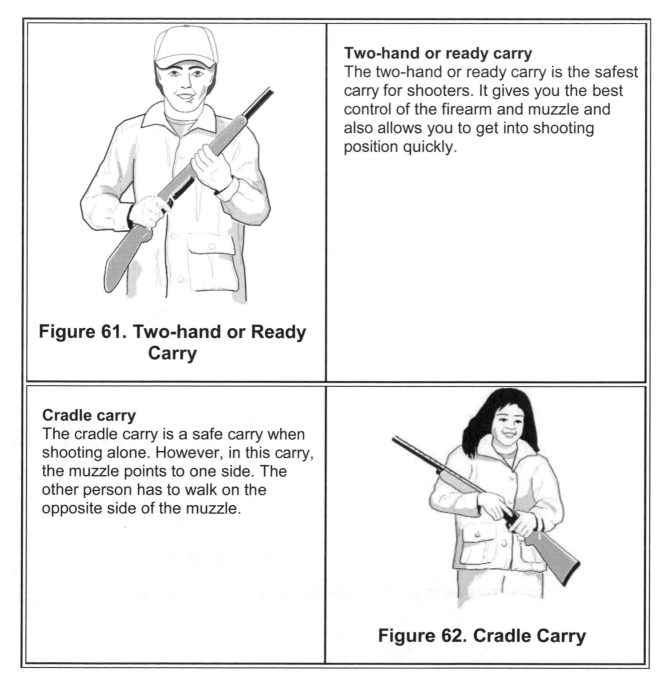

Two-hand or ready carry
The two-hand or ready carry is the safest carry for shooters. It gives you the best control of the firearm and muzzle and also allows you to get into shooting position quickly.

Figure 61. Two-hand or Ready Carry

Cradle carry
The cradle carry is a safe carry when shooting alone. However, in this carry, the muzzle points to one side. The other person has to walk on the opposite side of the muzzle.

Figure 62. Cradle Carry

Figure 63. Elbow or Side Carry (action open)

Elbow or side carry
The elbow or side carry is safe when walking in open terrain. However, do not use the side carry when walking through bush. Branches can get tangled around the firearm and push the barrel towards you. Do not use the side carry when others are ahead of you.

Trail carry
The trail carry is best used when you are alone or standing still. Otherwise, it is not recommended.

Figure 64. Trail Carry

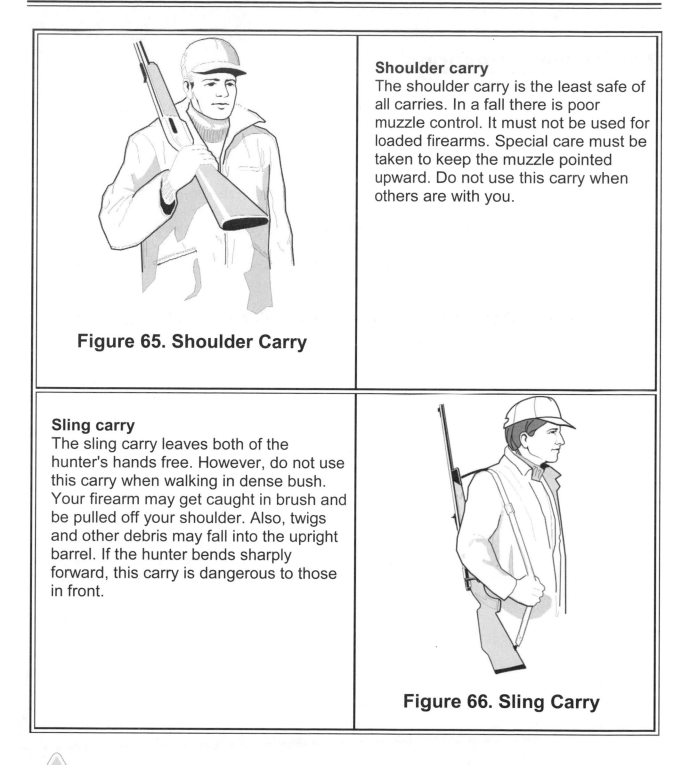

Shoulder carry

The shoulder carry is the least safe of all carries. In a fall there is poor muzzle control. It must not be used for loaded firearms. Special care must be taken to keep the muzzle pointed upward. Do not use this carry when others are with you.

Figure 65. Shoulder Carry

Sling carry

The sling carry leaves both of the hunter's hands free. However, do not use this carry when walking in dense bush. Your firearm may get caught in brush and be pulled off your shoulder. Also, twigs and other debris may fall into the upright barrel. If the hunter bends sharply forward, this carry is dangerous to those in front.

Figure 66. Sling Carry

Which carry you use will depend on where your companions are and the kind of terrain that you are walking on. Never use a carry that will cause the muzzle to be pointed at another person.

7.9. Review questions

1. List the two items of personal protective equipment one is required to wear before entering a gun range.

2. List the four procedures to follow when the "cease-fire" command is given.

3. What direction is safe to point your firearm, when on the firing line?

4. What is the supervision responsibility for minors on a gun range?

5. You must agree on who shoots where, when shooting outdoors with a group. This is called the…?

6. List the carrying positions for firearms and their direction of discharge if the firearm was to accidentally fire.

MODULE 8:

FIRING TECHNIQUES AND PROCEDURES FOR NON-RESTRICTED FIREARMS

MODULE 8: FIRING TECHNIQUES AND PROCEDURES FOR NON-RESTRICTED FIREARMS

8.0. Introduction to marksmanship

a. Marksmanship is the ability to hit your mark or target. Good marksmanship is important for safe shooting. If you are not certain where the bullet will go, how can the shot be safe?

b. Marksmanship depends on many factors, including anticipation, shooting position, aim, trigger control, controlled breathing and follow-through. These factors are discussed in this module.

8.1. Anticipation

When using a firearm, you must always be thinking about the possible situations and shots that may occur. The following are some examples:

- Will game appear suddenly?

- Where are the others in my shooting group?

- Is there a chance that the bullet will be deflected by a tree, a rock or water?

- Could someone be just over that hill?

- Where will the bullet go if it passes completely through the target?

 Always judge the possible results of every shot carefully before firing.

8.2. Shooting positions

8.2.0. Overview

⚠ **If you are left-handed, reverse the procedures for each shooting position. Left-handed shooters should consider using firearms that are manufactured specifically for left-handed use.**

8.2.1. Rifles

The four shooting positions for rifles are as follows:

1. standing position;

2. kneeling position;

3. sitting position; and

4. prone position.

Standing position

a. The standing position is the least stable shooting position from which to fire.

b. To shoot from the standing position, first, turn your body approximately 45° to the right of the target. Place your feet shoulder width apart. Support the rifle with your left arm and hand. Hold the left arm against your body for extra support where possible. Hold the stock firmly against your shoulder with the right hand. Keep holding the rifle firmly but not tightly.

c. If there is too much movement, do not shoot. Rest or support the rifle on a stable object such as a tree or large rock. In such situations, padding beneath the firearm is recommended. Using a sling will help steady your shot.

Figure 67. Standing Position

2. Kneeling position

a. The kneeling position is better than the standing position but not as steady as either the prone or the sitting positions.

b. Turn to about a 45° angle to the target. Kneel on your right knee and place your left foot slightly forward. Sit on the heel or the side of the right foot. Place the left elbow near you but not on the bony part of the left knee, as far under the rifle as you can.

Figure 68. Kneeling Position

3. Sitting position

a. The sitting position is one of the steadiest shooting positions.

b. Sit solidly on the ground, with your legs crossed or open, and your body positioned about 30° to the right of the line of aim.

c. Place your left elbow near, but not on, the bony part of the left knee. Tuck the elbow as far under the rifle as possible. Place the right elbow on or near the right knee.

d. Hold the rifle firmly but do not grip it tightly. If bracing your body against a tree or rock to steady your aim, be careful that the recoil will not force you against the support.

Figure 69. Sitting Position

4. Prone position

a. **The prone position is the steadiest shooting position.**

b. It is good for firing accurate long distance shots if tall grass or dense brush does not obscure the line of sight to the target.

c. Lie on your stomach with your body angled slightly to the left of the line of aim. Keep your back straight and legs in a relaxed position. The right leg should be bent slightly. Both elbows should be bent and your shoulders curved slightly forward to form a solid upper-body position. The upper body and arms support the rifle weight.

d. When shooting, you can use a rifle sling for extra support. Hold the rifle grip with the trigger hand. Place your opposite arm through the sling as far as it will go. Swing your arm in an outward circular motion, ending with your hand under the fore-stock of the rifle and the sling across the back of your hand.

Figure 70. Prone Position

8.2.2. Shotguns

a. Shooting a shotgun is different from shooting a rifle. With a rifle you aim precisely. With a shotgun you point at the target (Figure 71). Some shotguns are equipped with adjustable sights and are primarily used to fire slugs.

b. Accurate shotgun shooting requires you to make a fast but smooth series of movements of the eyes, body and firearm. To achieve this, stand like a boxer: feet spread apart, well-balanced, arms and body free to swing right or left. This position allows rapid movement.

c. When firing, shift your body weight to the leading leg. The leading hand holds the shotgun fore-stock and points naturally to the target area. Point the shotgun at the target and slap the trigger. With moving targets, continue to follow through as you fire. Otherwise, the shot will miss behind the target.

d. Naturally, this does not apply when hunting with a rifled barrel.

Figure 71. Shotgun Shooting Position

169

8.3. Aiming your firearm

8.3.0. Overview

a. Most sights are mounted on the top of the barrel (Figure 72). Their purpose is to help the shooter aim accurately.

b. There are four main types of sights:

- open sights;

- peep sights;

- telescopic sights; and

- electronic sights.

c. Rifles and shotguns may have any of these types.

d. Most shotguns only have a bead mounted on the front of the barrel. This serves as a front sight. Your eye becomes the rear sight.

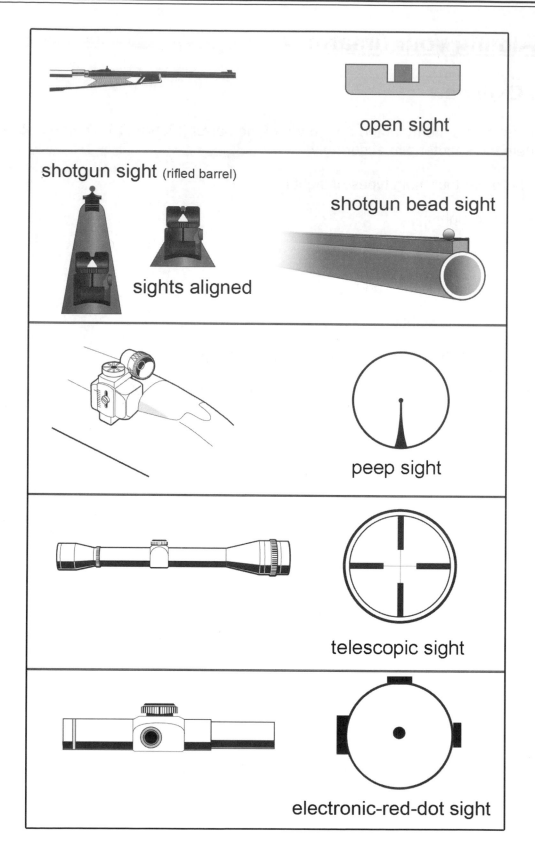

open sight

shotgun sight (rifled barrel)

sights aligned

shotgun bead sight

peep sight

telescopic sight

electronic-red-dot sight

Figure 72. Types of Sights

8.3.1. Aiming rifles

! **All firearms must be sighted-in for the individual prior to use.**

a. Use your master eye for sighting. It is the stronger of your two eyes and will judge speed and range. It will focus more accurately (see section 8.4.1).

b. You must also learn to correctly use your firearm's sight if your aim is to be accurate. Open sights require you to physically line up both rear and front sights with the target. This process is called **sight alignment**. When you aim any sight at a target, **a sight picture** is created.

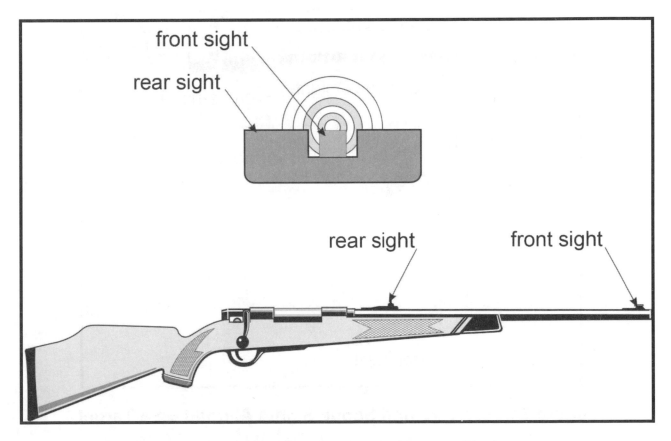

front sight

rear sight

rear sight

front sight

Figure 73. Open Sights Aligned on a Target

c. Scope and electronic red-dot sights do not require conscious alignment. Scope sights also have the advantage of magnifying your view of the target.

d. When preparing to aim through a scope or electronic red-dot sight, do not look away from the target and then try to find the target again by looking through the scope. Instead, while steadily watching the target, mount the firearm correctly to your shoulder pointing the firearm toward the target area until the scope comes up naturally between your eye and the target. Keep your eye well clear of the sight when firing.

⚠ **Scope sights have a very narrow field of view, so you might not see a person or object coming into the path of your shot. Never use a mounted scope as a substitute for binoculars to identify persons, animals or objects.**

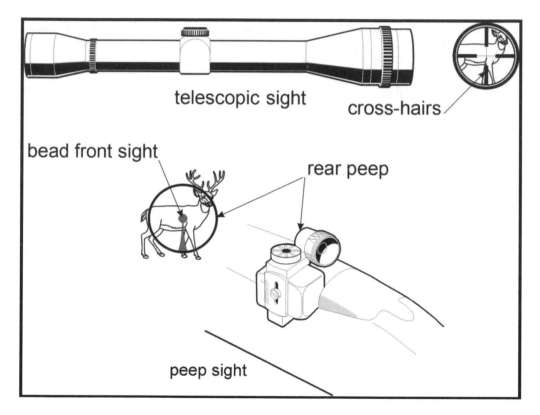

Figure 74. Aperture and Scope Sights Aligned on a Target

8.3.2. Pointing shotguns

a. Pointing a shotgun is different from aiming other firearms. With a rifle, you must aim precisely. With a shotgun, you point at the target. When a shotgun is fired, the shot pellets spread out after leaving the barrel and hit a larger area than a single bullet. Therefore, precise aiming is not as necessary as with a rifle.

b. When using a shotgun, keep both eyes open. Focus on the moving target, not on the firearm barrel or the bead sight. While watching the target, place the shotgun to your shoulder and point it toward the target area. Be sure to place the stock against your cheek first, then against your shoulder. This positions the firearm in exactly the same position each time you shoot.

c. Some shotguns are equipped with adjustable sights and are primarily used to fire slugs. For this type of shotgun, use the same aiming techniques as you would for a rifle.

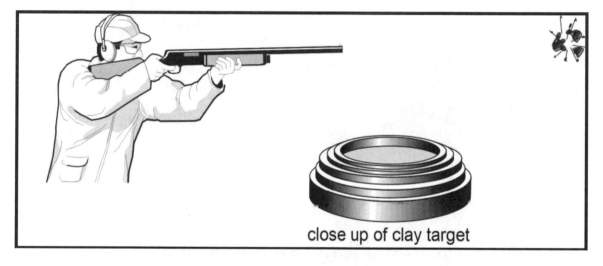

close up of clay target

Figure 75. Shotgun Sight Alignment

8.4. Fundamentals of shooting

8.4.1. Sight alignment

⚠ To find out which is your master eye, create a triangle using both hands as illustrated in Figure 76. With both eyes open, view an object in the distance from the centre of the triangle. With both eyes remaining open, and keeping the object within the triangle, close the left eye and then open the left eye. Then, close the right eye and then open the right eye. The master eye will keep the object in the centre of the triangle.

Figure 76. Determining your Master Eye

8.4.2. Breathing as it relates to shot release

a. Holding one's breath is not natural. It's not possible to judge how much air is held for each shot release, since there is no gauge on the lungs. The shot must be released in the natural pause of the breathing cycle.

b. We breathe in, we breathe out. There is a natural pause at the bottom of each exhale. It is this natural pause (2.5 seconds) that the shot must be released in. In order to lengthen this natural pause, the shooter has to breathe in deep, force the breath out deeper than normal, breathe in deep again, this time let the breath out normally. The natural pause in the breathing cycle has just been increased to approximately 8.5 seconds. That is plenty of time to confirm sight picture and release the shot, if not, just repeat the process. Breathe in deep, force it out, breathe in deep again, let it out NATURALLY and squeeze the shot off.

c. Figure 77 has been in circulation for over forty years. Unfortunately, some people will sometimes misinterpret it and wrongfully revert to holding their breath.

175

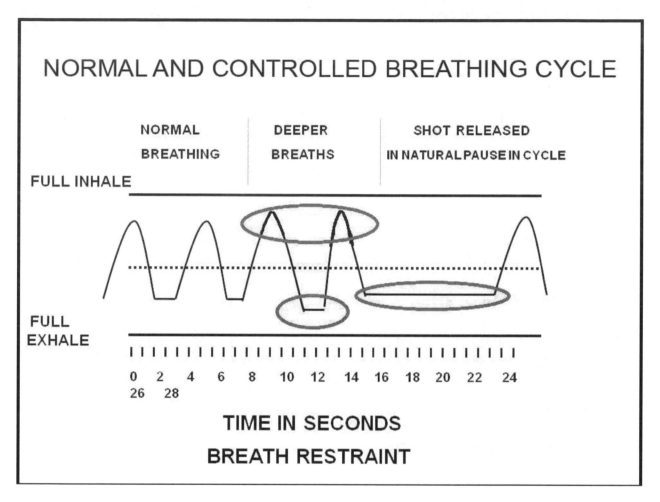

Figure 77. Normal and Controlled Breathing Cycle

8.4.3. Trigger control

Trigger control is essential for accurate shooting.

a. Rifles

When the sights are aligned on the target, squeeze the trigger slowly and steadily. Avoid yanking or pulling. Anything other than a smooth squeeze will cause the firearm to move and send the shot off target. Relax before the firearm fires to allow each shot to happen almost as a "surprise."

b. Shotguns

Shotgun triggers are slapped instead of squeezed. The trigger slap is similar to the action of striking a typewriter key. Slap the trigger quickly, but not hard.

8.4.4. Follow-through

This means maintaining your sight picture and/or shooting position after discharging the firearm. If you do not follow-through, it is more likely that your shot will be "off target."

8.5. Targets

8.5.1. Acceptable targets

- A target that is positively identified
- A target that is safe to shoot at
- A target that can be lawfully shot

8.5.2. Unacceptable targets

- A target that you are not sure of, cannot clearly see and cannot identify
- A target that cannot be shot safely
- A target that is not legal to shoot

⚠ Check with local or provincial authorities for specific rules and regulations.

8.6 Review questions

1. It is important to always judge the possible results of every shot carefully before firing. True or false?

2. Name the four shooting positions for rifles.

3. Describe the importance of determining your master eye.

4. What is an acceptable target?

5. Why is trigger control essential for accurate shooting?

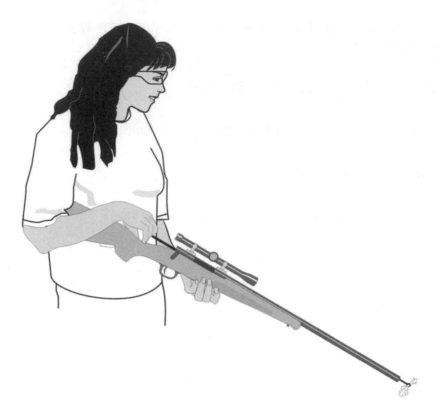

MODULE 9:
CARE OF NON-RESTRICTED FIREARMS

MODULE 9: CARE OF NON-RESTRICTED FIREARMS

9.1. Firearm servicing

⚠️ **Ensure that all firearms are unloaded and ACTS/PROVE it safe before attempting to clean. Refer to Module 6 for information on unloading procedures. ACTS and PROVE it safe.**

a. Always be sure your firearm is functioning properly. A firearm that does not work properly is an unsafe firearm.

b. This module on minor maintenance and servicing procedures for your firearm is included for general information only. Specific information on cleaning and servicing your firearm is available in your firearm owner's manual, at a gun shop or from a gunsmith. Incidents can occur if these procedures are not performed correctly.

c. Firearms are precision instruments. Even minor repairs should be made by qualified individuals. Unqualified persons should never try to repair or modify any firearm.

d. The average user should do basic cleaning and lubrication only.

Example of an Incident

Someone was preparing to clean a loaded firearm with the action closed, and dropped it. The rifle fired when it hit the floor. Someone in the next room was killed.

The contributing factor was as follows:
- failing to **ACTS/PROVE** the firearm.

9.2. Firearm cleaning

9.2.0. Overview

a. Information on cleaning firearms safely may be obtained from your firearm owner's manual. If you do not have one, contact the manufacturer. Incidents can happen if the cleaning procedure is not performed correctly.

b. The two major threats to firearm safety are the following:

- rust caused by moisture and condensation; and

- excessive build-up of residue or rust in the firearm.

c. Either may cause excessive pressure, damaging the barrel. This is why regular cleaning is recommended.

d. The barrel of a firearm should be cleaned after every use. This will protect its finish. It will also help keep it in good working order. For instructions on cleaning the rest of the firearm, consult your owner's manual.

e. Modern smokeless primers and powders are non-corrosive. However, some older military surplus ammunition still contains corrosive chemicals. If you use corrosive ammunition, you should clean your firearm immediately after you use it.

f. Any firearm that has been stored for a long time must be cleaned thoroughly before use. Cleaning before using is required when the firearm has been exposed to moisture or dirt.

If cleaning your firearm requires disassembly, consult your owner's manual. You should wear safety glasses when cleaning or dissembling a firearm. Oil or moisture can be very dangerous in cold weather. They may cause safeties and other firing mechanism parts to freeze in a firing position. Later, when the firearm thaws, it may fire. Residue or rust in the chamber or barrel may cause serious pressure build-up. Also, oil may mix with unburnt powder and other dirt, causing the firearm to jam.

9.2.1. Cleaning materials

a. To clean a firearm properly, you need the following materials:

- a cleaning rod or a pull-through and attachments (be sure to use the right size for the firearm), such as:

  o a bore brush,

  o tips to hold cloth patches;

- patches;

- powder solvent (also called "bore cleaner");

- gun oil; and

- a soft cloth.

b. If possible, clean your firearm from the breech toward the muzzle. Avoid cleaning from the muzzle toward the breech (Figures 78 and 79).

c. However, you may have to clean some types from the muzzle end. In this case, lock the breech open. This permits the passage of the cleaning rod completely through the barrel. You will find a pull-through cleaning device helpful. Avoid rubbing the cleaning rod on the muzzle. Damage to the muzzle may occur. It is beneficial to insert a cloth into the open action to collect residue, to prevent dirt from entering the action, and to prevent damage to the firearm.

d. When cleaning a bolt action, remove the bolt, if possible. Clean the firearm from the breech end. Some firearms are easier to clean if you remove the barrel first.

While cleaning a firearm, remember and follow the Vital Four ACTS— PROVE it safe. The following additional recommended practices for home safety with firearms might prevent incidents:

- **Make sure no ammunition is nearby during cleaning.**

- **Never allow a loaded firearm in any building or living area.**

- **Always give cleaning your firearm your full attention. Never clean a firearm while doing something else, like watching television.**

9.2.2. Cleaning procedures

The firearms cleaning procedures are as follows:

1. ACTS and PROVE it safe.

2. Attach the bore brush to the cleaning rod. Apply bore cleaner to the brush.

3. Run the brush through the bore of the firearm barrel several times. Be sure that the brush sticks out from the barrel completely. Then, draw it back through the barrel (Figure 78).

4. Remove the bore brush from the cleaning rod. Attach a patch-holder tip and a proper size cloth patch. Pour solvent on the cloth patch. Run it through the bore several times. Remove the cloth patch from the rod tip.

5. Next, run a clean, dry patch through the bore several times.

6. If the patch comes out dirty, repeat the first four steps. Do this until a patch finally comes through clean.

7. Next, run a lightly oiled patch through the bore. Use only light gun oil.

8. Wipe the outside of the firearm with a clean cloth and apply a light coat of gun oil or rust preventative to the metal surfaces. You should also maintain the condition of the stock by applying the appropriate treatment (consult the owner's manual).

9. Always store your firearm properly.

10. Don't forget to clean your magazine.

11. Remember, before the next firing of the firearm, run a dry patch through the barrel to remove any oil.

 Make sure you wash your hands after the cleaning procedure.

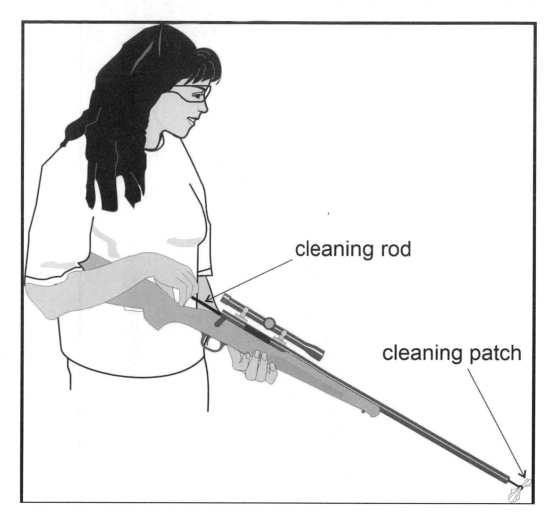

cleaning rod

cleaning patch

Figure 78. Cleaning a Rifle Barrel from the Breech to the Muzzle

 After cleaning a firearm for storage, avoid skin contact with metal parts. Acids in perspiration can cause rust.

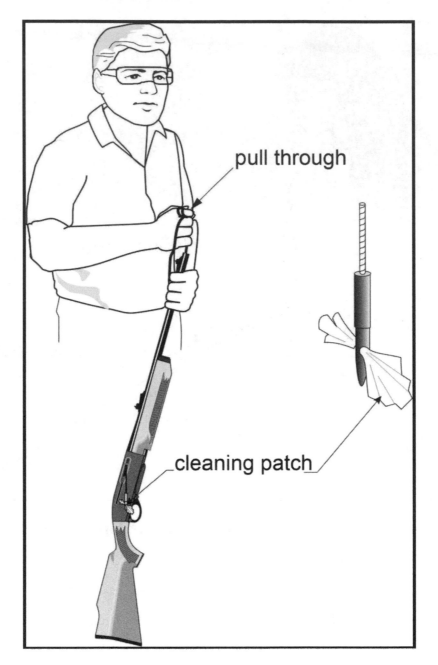

pull through

cleaning patch

Figure 79. Cleaning a Rifle

9.2.3. Ammunition storage

a. Ammunition should also be kept clean and dry. Oil, sand or dirt on the cartridge or shell can damage the firearm. It could also cause jamming of the action.

b. Avoid exposing your ammunition to heat and vibration. Powder can decay and become unpredictable if exposed to excessive heat and long-term vibration.

Primers are adversely affected by exposure to penetrating oils. Do not clean your ammunition with an oily rag. Before using any firearm, remove oil or grease from inside the barrel. Increased pressure caused by dirt or oil may cause the barrel to burst. This comes from the pressure generated in a dirty barrel when a bullet is fired through it. After storage, and before you use the firearm again, run a clean patch through the bore. Remove all grease and oil. Always ensure that your firearm is in good working order. Ensure that you have followed the Vital Four ACTS in order to PROVE it safe before attempting to clean and throughout the entire cleaning procedure. Refer to Module 6: Operating Firearms Actions on Unloading Procedures.

9.3. Review questions

1. Describe the mandatory procedure before servicing a firearm.

2. Where do we find directions on disassembly and lubrication for a specific firearm?

3. What is the risk caused by excess oil and grease inside the barrel?

4. What effect does penetrating oil have on ammunition primers?

MODULE 10:

SOCIAL RESPONSIBILITIES OF THE FIREARM OWNER/USER

MODULE 10: SOCIAL RESPONSIBILITIES OF THE FIREARM OWNER/USER

10.1. Firearm-related incidents

a. The main purpose of this course is to promote the safe use and handling of firearms. Increased safety awareness will help prevent both the unintentional and deliberate misuse of firearms.

b. Most safety courses concentrate on the prevention of an unintentional discharge when handling firearms. A firearm generally causes more serious injuries than any other type of weapon.

c. Suicides and homicides are often acts of sudden impulse. Many of them might not have happened if the firearms and ammunition were stored safely. For this reason, this course stresses the safe handling and use of non-restricted firearms and ammunition and their secure storage.

10.2. Intentional misuse of firearms

10.2.0. Overview

a. The intentional misuse of firearms, resulting in suicide and homicide, has fallen since the eighties. Misuse of firearms, resulting in unintentional discharge, has also fallen.

b. The misuse of firearms can lead to tragic results. The same applies to the misuse of automobiles, power tools and even kitchen knives.

10.2.1. Signs of risk

a. You can sometimes anticipate violent situations before they happen. Remember, these events can happen in our own homes, those of friends or neighbours.

b. When these situations seem to be developing, it is good practice to remove all firearms. This is true even when firearms are properly stored. Consider storing the firearms at an alternate location, and if necessary, notify the police of the situation.

c. Consider notifying your CFO through the public safety line at 1-800-731-4000.

d. You would not hesitate to prevent a friend or relative from drinking and driving. Do not hesitate to prevent the misuse of firearms.

e. Your CFO will determine the continued eligibility of individuals to keep firearms.

⚠ **In an emergency, for public or your own safety, immediately contact your local police service. In case of concern for public or your own safety, contact 1-800-731-4000.**

10.3. Firearms reported lost, missing or stolen

Owners of firearms are required under the *Criminal Code* to report the loss or theft of their firearms.

Report the loss or theft of a firearm:

- to your local police service; and

- the CFP at 1-800-731-4000.

10.4. Secure storage

a. Secure storage is the best way to limit theft and deliberate misuse of firearms. It should not be easy for unauthorized individuals to gain access to firearms and ammunition.

b. Do not leave the key or combination to the firearm storage area or container lying around. Do not give them out to others. Also, do not let it become widely known that you have firearms.

c. Locking up firearms and ammunition is important and is required by the *Firearms Act* and its Regulations. If you require more information, please refer to it.

d. Make access to firearms and ammunition difficult. If firearms and ammunition are difficult to get, there may be a delay in acting on the impulse to do harm. This delay may be enough to make the impulse decrease or go away.

e. Secure storage of firearms and ammunition may act as a deterrent to easy theft by criminals. **Remember: you are legally and morally responsible for your firearms 24 hours a day.** By law, you must store them safely and securely when you are not physically in control of them. This may cause some inconvenience, but it may also save a person from death or serious injury.

> Please refer to **MODULE 11**: SAFE STORAGE DISPLAY, TRANSPORTATION AND HANDLING OF NON-RESTRICTED FIREARMS.

Unsafe storage of firearms is a criminal offence. Unsafely stored firearms may be misused. You and you alone will be held accountable (i.e., criminal negligence causing death, bodily harm).

191

10.5. Firearm hazards and precautions

This table summarizes some firearm hazards and appropriate precautions to take.

Table 8. Firearm hazards and precautions

Hazards	Precautions
Access by unqualified or unauthorized users	• Disable action before storage or transport (or use trigger or cable lock) • Store firearms in a safely locked cabinet or container, out of view • Store ammunition separately and out of view • Supervise unqualified users
Unintentional discharge	• Control muzzle direction at all times • Unload firearm when not in immediate use • Open action when handling • Keep finger off trigger and out of the trigger guard except when firing • Safety ON • No horseplay • A malfunctioning firearm may result in unintentional discharge • Ensure your firearm is well maintained and regularly serviced
Wrong ammunition	• Carry only correct ammunition • Check ammunition against firearm data stamp • Use proper ammunition for target and conditions • If reloading, follow correct procedures • Improperly loaded ammunition can cause a firearm incident • Ensure you know how to load correctly
Ricochets	• Be extra cautious when shooting at, or towards flat or hard surfaces • Check area near, or behind target before firing • Be extra cautious when shooting at, or towards water
Wrong target	• Identify target before firing and be sure, before you shoot • Know what is behind the target • Make sure the backstop is adequate

 Follow the Vital Four ACTS—PROVE it safe.

10.6. Social responsibilities and ethics

a. As a firearm user, you have certain legal obligations to the community at large. In some cases, however, sticking to the letter of the law is not enough. The spirit of the law must also be followed. The welfare and well-being of your fellow citizens must come first.

b. Below are some moral and social rules. They must be part of the code of ethics for anyone possessing firearms.

   - Store all firearms and ammunition properly. Keep your firearms and ammunition properly secured and out of sight.

   - Explain firearm safety to all family members. Everyone in a home where firearms are kept should know the safety rules. Firearms are no different than dangerous tools or poisons in the home. Proper use and handling of firearms and ammunition must be taught to the entire family. The key or combination number to secure locking devices should be kept away from, and out of the reach of, children and unauthorized adults.

   - Remove firearms from situations of potential violence. You may become aware of a situation where violence or tragedy could occur. In such cases, it is wise to go beyond the safe storage of firearms. Completely remove firearms that may be present. If this is not possible, at least notify the police of the situation.

   - Act sensibly and carefully while around firearms. Always pay close attention to what you and others around you are doing. Make sure that everyone is acting safely and responsibly.

   - Never consume drugs or alcoholic beverages when around firearms. Do not go shooting with anyone who has. Alcohol and drugs can affect your mental or physical reactions. Both prescription and non-prescription drugs can affect your alertness, senses and balance. Some types of allergy medicines are a good example. Always stay fully alert when around firearms.

   - Always get permission before shooting on someone else's property. Make sure that you are welcome and permitted before you shoot anywhere. Do this whether the land belongs to the crown, to a local club or to a private citizen. Make sure that you can shoot there safely. For example, someone else may be shooting there at the same time. Check with local authorities.

   - Have your eyesight checked regularly. Shooting requires good vision for target identification and accuracy. Be sure of your target and beyond.

   - Maintain your firearm in good working order. If required, have a qualified gunsmith service your firearm.

193

- Avoid firing near buildings or roads. Respect the rights of others to safe travel and undisturbed use of their property. Only shoot near buildings with authorized permission, and only if it is legal and safe.

- Know and respect firearms regulations and local by-laws.

- Wear safety equipment. Encourage others to do the same. Safety equipment may include, but should not be limited to, sight and hearing protection, gloves, caps and proper clothing.

10.7. Review questions

1. Is there a time when a gun owner does not have a moral or a legal responsibility for his firearm?

2. List five hazards that could potentially cause firearm injuries and fatalities.

3. List three ethical responsibilities of a firearm's owner.

4. What is the most positive influence in the prevention of firearm incidents?

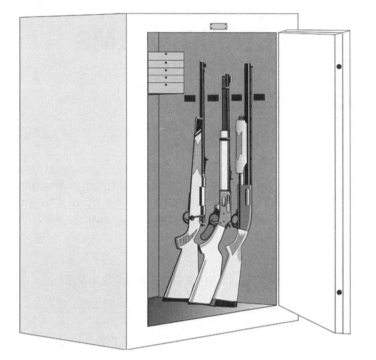

MODULE 11:

SAFE STORAGE, DISPLAY, TRANSPORTATION AND HANDLING OF NON-RESTRICTED FIREARMS

MODULE 11: SAFE STORAGE, DISPLAY, TRANSPORTATION AND HANDLING OF NON-RESTRICTED FIREARMS

11.1. Classes of firearms

11.1.0. Overview

The table below provides a brief description of non-restricted firearms. For legal references, however, please refer to the *Firearms Act* and its Regulations, and Part III of the *Criminal Code* for a description of restricted and prohibited classes. Call 1-800-731-4000 for further information.

Table 18. Non-restricted Firearms

Non-restricted Firearms
Generally, firearms commonly used for hunting or sporting purposes such as target shooting are included in this class. The following are examples of non-restricted firearms: • rifles; and • shotguns.

⚠ **It must be noted that some rifles and shotguns are considered restricted or prohibited. Persons wishing to acquire such firearms should contact a firearms officer for further information.**

11.2. Ammunition

11.2.0. Overview

For a complete description of ammunition, prohibited ammunition and prohibited devices, consult Part III of the *Criminal Code* of Canada. Call 1-800-731-4000 for additional information.

11.2.1. Ammunition

Is a cartridge containing a projectile designed to be discharged from a firearm. This includes caseless cartridges and shot shells.

11.2.2. Prohibited ammunition

Individuals cannot acquire prohibited ammunition that is designed, manufactured or altered to ignite on impact.

11.2.3. Prohibited devices

Individuals cannot acquire prohibited devices; i.e., high-capacity magazine (except for rim-fire cartridges), silencer.

Refer to the appropriate sections of the *Firearms Act* and its Regulations for detailed requirements relating to the storage, display, transportation and handling of non-restricted firearms.

a. Remember, you are responsible for your firearms 24 hours a day. Anyone who owns or uses a firearm must meet safe storage, display, transportation and handling requirements. These requirements are set out in the *Storage, Display, Transportation and Handling of Firearms by individuals Regulations*. All of these are described in this module.

b. Firearm owners and users should always assume that anyone untrained in the safe handling and use of firearms does not know how to handle firearms safely. Serious incidents could occur from unauthorized access, especially where children are concerned. To prevent this, always store, display, transport and handle firearms and ammunition in accordance with the regulations.

c. Remember, the law requires that all firearms must be unloaded except when in use.

11.3. Storage

a. A non-restricted firearm may be stored only under the following conditions:

1. It is unloaded by the **ACTS and PROVE it safe**, and either:

- rendered inoperable by using a secure locking device; or

- by removing the bolt or bolt-carrier; or

- stored in a securely locked opaque container, receptacle, or room that cannot be easily broken open or into (Figures 80-82).

2. It is not within easy access to ammunition, unless the ammunition is stored, together with or separately from the firearm, in a securely locked container or receptacle that cannot be easily broken open or into.

 Keep in mind that storing ammunition in an unvented container may create an explosive hazard during a fire.

b. In areas where it is legal to discharge a firearm, a non-restricted firearm used for predator control may be stored temporarily unlocked, and out in the open, as long as it is unloaded, and not readily accessible to ammunition.

c. In a remote area where hunting might reasonably occur, a non-restricted firearm may be stored unlocked, out in the open and accessible to ammunition as long as the firearm is unloaded.

Figure 80. Safe

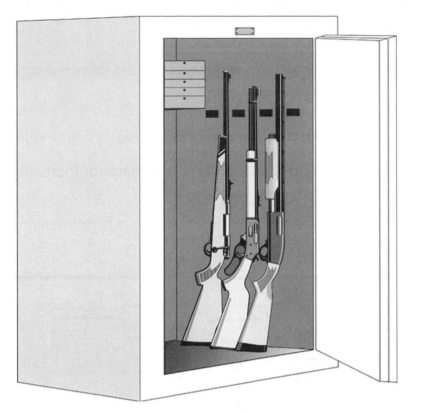

Figure 81. Secure Cabinet/vault

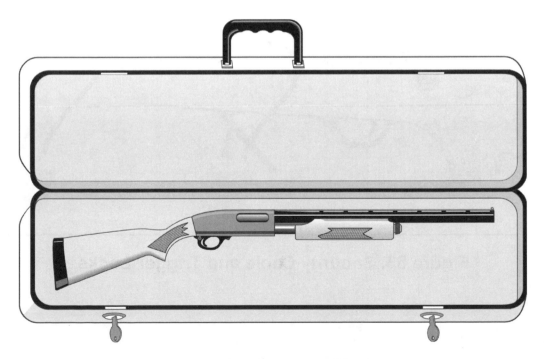

Figure 82. Storage Case

11.4. Display

A non-restricted firearm may be displayed only under the following conditions:

1. It is unloaded, and:

   • rendered inoperable by using a secure locking device (Figure 83); or

   • stored in a securely locked container, receptacle or room that cannot be easily broken open or into (Figures 80-82).

2. It is not displayed with and not within easy access to ammunition that can be discharged from it (Figure 84).

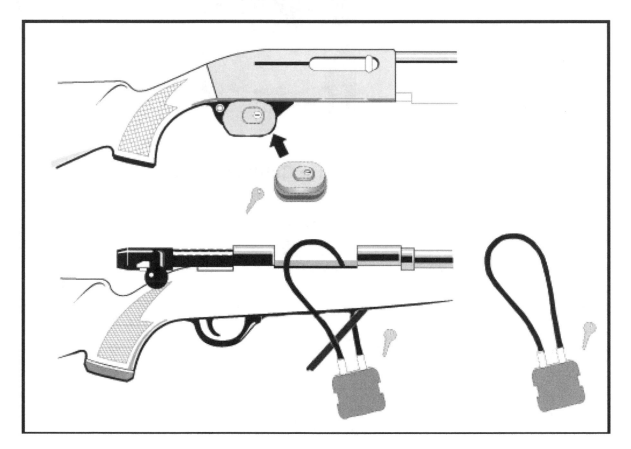

Figure 83. Security Cable and Trigger Locks

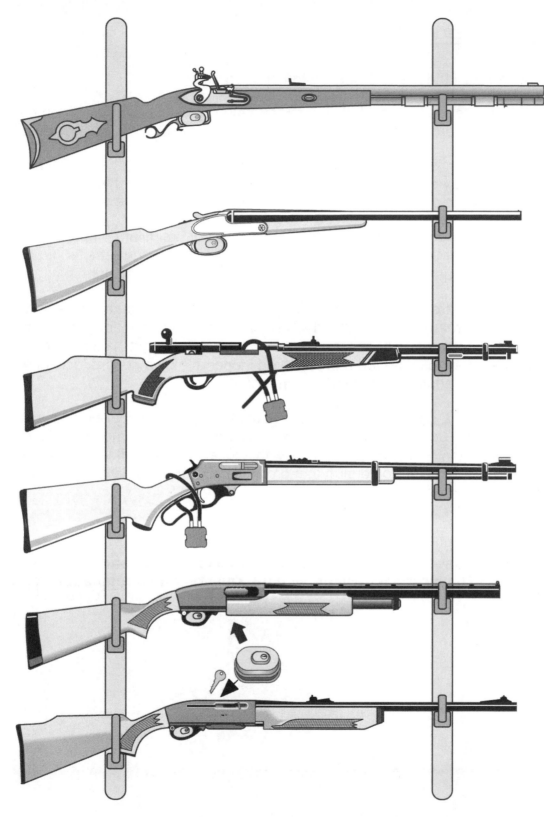

Figure 84. Display

11.5. Transportation

a. A non-restricted firearm must be transported unloaded.

b. However, loaded muzzleloading firearms may be transported between hunting sites if the percussion cap or flint is removed—subject to provincial/territorial regulations.

c. You may leave a non-restricted firearm in an unattended vehicle if it is unloaded and placed in a locked trunk or a similar compartment of the vehicle.

d. If the unattended vehicle does not have a trunk or a similar compartment, lock the vehicle or the part of the vehicle that contains the non-restricted firearm and leave the non-restricted firearm inside, unloaded and out of sight.

e. In a remote area when hunting might reasonably occur, you may leave a non-restricted firearm in an unattended vehicle that has no trunk or compartment that can be locked (i.e., canoe, snowmobile), if it is out of sight. The non-restricted firearm must be unloaded and rendered inoperable by a secure locking device unless you require it for predator control.

f. If you live in a rural area and need reasonable access to your non-restricted firearm for predator control, you may be exempted from some of the storage and transportation requirements. Check with a local firearms officer, a wildlife or conservation officer to confirm that provincial or municipal laws allow storage on a temporary basis.

If you want to transport firearms on an aircraft, you should first contact the air carrier. The air carrier will provide information on its regulations and requirements.

Every person commits an offence who, without lawful excuse, points a firearm at another person, whether the firearm is loaded or unloaded, and is:

1. **guilty of an indictable offence and liable to imprisonment for a term not exceeding five years; or**

2. **guilty of an offence punishable on summary conviction (a fine of $5,000 and/or six months imprisonment).**

Reference: Subsections 87(1) and (2) of Part III of the *Criminal Code*

They may also lose their firearm, lose their licence, receive a fine, receive jail time and/or be prohibited from possessing a firearm for a period of time.

Not all firearms laws are included in this Handbook. If you have any doubts about the Regulations, or if you need more information, contact the following:

- the RCMP website at www.rcmp-grc.gc.ca/cfp; or
- the CFP at 1-800-731-4000.

11.6. Handling

a. Before obtaining a firearm, think about how you will carry it home and where you will keep it. Remember, when you leave the seller or dealer's shop, you will be carrying your firearm in a public place. It is recommended that all firearms be carried in a case or opaque container to avoid display in public (Figure 85). Consult your local authorities for details.

b. There are locations where having or discharging a firearm violates federal or provincial/territorial Acts and Regulations, or municipal bylaws. It may also be an offence to load or handle firearms in these places. You may load a firearm or handle a loaded firearm only in a place where it is lawful to discharge it.

⚠ **Only load a firearm when you intend to use it and only in an area where it can be safely and legally discharged. Always be sure of your target and beyond.**

Figure 85. Lockable Carrying/Storage Case

Every person commits an offence who, without lawful excuse, points a firearm at another person, whether the firearm is loaded or unloaded, and is:

1. guilty of an indictable offence and liable to imprisonment for a term not exceeding five years; or

2. guilty of an offence punishable on summary conviction (a fine of $5,000 and/or six months imprisonment).

Reference: Subsections 87(1) and (2) of Part III of the *Criminal Code*

They may also lose their firearm, lose their licence, receive a fine, receive jail time and/or be prohibited from possessing a firearm for a period of time.

11.7. Review questions

1. List three rules you must follow in order to legally display a firearm.

2. Name two devices used for permanent firearm storage and two devices used for temporary storage.

3. Name one type of prohibited ammunition and two types of prohibited firearm accessories.

4. List three rules you must follow in order to legally transport non-restricted firearms.

5. What is the penalty for a person who transgresses the laws of safe storage, safe transport, and/or safe handling of firearms?

CANADIAN FIREARMS PROGRAM

CANADIAN RESTRICTED FIREARMS SAFETY COURSE

2014

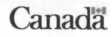

Library and Archives Canada Cataloguing in Publication

Canadian Restricted Firearms Safety Course Modules: Student Handbook, 5th edition

Also available in French under the title: Cours canadien de sécurité dans le maniement des armes à feu à autorisation restreinte : Manuel de l'étudiant.

(*Également disponible en français sous le titre, Cours canadien de sécurité dans le maniement des armes à feu à autorisation restreinte : Manuel de l`étudiant.*)

ISBN 978-0-660-19945-0

Catalogue number: PS99-2/1-1-2014E

Firearms—Canada—Safety measures.

Firearms ownership—Canada.

Firearms—Safety measures.

Gun control—Canada.

Royal Canadian Mounted Police (RCMP) / Canadian Firearms Program (CFP)

TS532.2.C36 2010 363.330971 C2008-980104-0

This edition of the Canadian Restricted Firearms Safety Course is produced by:

RCMP Headquarters
Ottawa ON K1A 0R2
Canada

Fax: 613-825-0297

PREFACE

Acknowledgements

Many organizations with an ongoing interest in firearms safety volunteered their time to review and comment on this Handbook during its review stages. The efforts and assistance of the many people involved (see below) are acknowledged and appreciated. Without their help and that of the following persons, this Handbook would not have been correctly reviewed:

- CFOs and their Staff

- Baldwin, Chris; Manager Conservation Services, Stewardship and Education Section Wildlife Division, Newfoundland & Labrador

- Batten, Shelly; Operations Manager, Firearms Safety Education Service of Ontario (FSESO), Ontario

- Cooper, A.C. (Tony); Firearms Safety Education Service of Ontario (FSESO), Ontario

- Halvorson, Tony; CFSC & CRFSC Master Instructor, Prince Edward Island

- Jones, Don; Chief Instructor, Retired, Firearms Safety Education Service of Ontario (FSESO), Ontario

- Martin, Allan; President, Instructors of Firearms Safety Association (IOFSA) of British Columbia, CFSC & CRFSC Master Instructor, British Columbia

- Sadauskas, Sherrie (McAdam); Firearms Officer, Halton Regional Police Service, Chief Instructor, Firearms Safety Education Service of Ontario (FSESO)

- Tousignant, Gerald; President, Fédération québécoise de Tir, Québec and all his team.

- Valiquette, Jean; Master Instructor (CFSC) for the Fédération québécoise des chasseurs et pêcheurs, Sécurité nature, for the province of Québec

Most importantly, the RCMP/CFP wishes to acknowledge the talent and expertise of the certified Instructors of the CRFSC from across Canada, many of whom took the time and effort to provide written recommendations and suggestions in the development of this material.

<u>Disclaimer</u>

The improper use of firearms may result in serious injury. The material presented in this Handbook is intended to demonstrate the operation of firearms in accordance with safe handling techniques and an awareness of manufacturers' specifications and safety features.

The RCMP/CFP makes no warranties whatsoever, either express or implied, oral or written, in fact or by operation of law or otherwise, regarding the safety of any firearm or the use of any safety mechanism shown in the Handbook.

Individuals should use firearms in accordance with manufacturers' specifications and contact individual manufacturers as each model features different safety mechanisms and some of the techniques demonstrated might not be appropriate for certain firearms.

Ultimately, responsibility for firearm safety rests with the individual.

INTRODUCTION TO THE RESTRICTED
FIREARMS SAFETY COURSE

INTRODUCTION TO THE CANADIAN RESTRICTED FIREARMS SAFETY COURSE

Overview

The Canadian Restricted Firearms Safety Course (CRFSC) is designed to apply to novice restricted firearm users. Existing firearms safety courses across Canada have a proven track record in the reduction of firearm-related incidents. However, these courses have been designed and delivered for firearms use in a specific activity. The CRFSC is an introductory firearms safety course intended for all new restricted firearm users and those individuals who wish to acquire restricted firearms.

The Canadian Firearms Program

The Canadian Firearms Program (CFP) is administered by the RCMP/CFP, which works with provincial CFOs and many community partners across the country in implementing the *Firearms Act* and its Regulations, and other related legislation regarding firearms.

The goal of the CFP is the safe and responsible use of firearms, and it includes a range of activities directed toward achieving that goal such as the following:

- the licensing of all firearm owners and businesses;
- the delivery of the CFSCs;
- public education regarding safe storage, transport and use of firearms; and
- import and export controls.

Licensing, registration and other Program information are recorded in the Canadian Firearms Information System, a national database that is managed by the RCMP/CFP. Certain information is available to law enforcement agencies to help them prevent and investigate firearms incidents and crime, consistent with the public safety objectives of the *Firearms Act.*

Your personal information is carefully protected by the CFP, consistent with the *Firearms Act* and its Regulations, federal and provincial privacy laws and other applicable statutes.

If you have any questions about the CFP, please contact us at the following location:

Canadian Firearms Program	
Telephone:	1-800-731-4000
Fax:	613-825-0297
E-mail:	cfp-pcaf@rcmp-grc.gc.ca
Address:	Royal Canadian Mounted Police / Canadian Firearms Program Ottawa ON K1A OR2

You can also consult the *Firearms Act* and its Regulations directly via the RCMP/CFP website.

The RCMP/CFP wishes you the best in following the CRFSC for the class(es) of firearms you wish to acquire and/or possess. Please note that all CRFSC instructors and examiners must be designated by the CFO for the province or territory in which you are taking the course.

Course Objectives

Firearm owners have social responsibilities. By completing this course, you will be instructed on what these responsibilities are. You will learn how to do the following:

- handle restricted firearms and ammunition safely;

- use restricted firearms and ammunition safely;

- comply with firearms laws;

- store restricted firearms and ammunition safely;

- display restricted firearms safely; and

- transport restricted firearms and ammunition safely.

The CRFSC consists of two parts. One is classroom instruction. The other is learning the material in this Handbook. There will be both written and practical examinations. Successfully passing them will demonstrate the knowledge and skills you have gained in the course. Live firing exercises, however, are not offered as part of this course.

During the course, some topics are discussed and explored several times. This will help you learn and retain the content. Leaving anything out of the course will reduce the amount you learn. This applies to all assignments, exercises or examinations given by your instructor.

The course emphasizes safe storage, display, transportation, handling and use of restricted firearms but safety depends on more than just safe physical actions.

Safe handling must include greater knowledge of the firearms themselves, ammunition, and the laws and regulations related to them.

Course Handbook

Safety also relies on your attitude about responsible handling and use of firearms. Pay close attention to the section on legal, ethical and social responsibilities. Your safety and that of the people around you depends on it.

This book is an essential part of the course. The other parts are the classroom lessons and practical exercises given by the instructor. Together, they will help you learn how to safely handle firearms.

This book contains the following elements:

- the **Vital Four ACTS** of firearm safety;

- a brief history of restricted firearms;

- information on restricted firearms and ammunition and how they work;

- instructions on how to pick up, handle and carry restricted firearms safely;

- descriptions of how to unload, load and fire restricted firearms safely;

- descriptions of firing positions;

- instructions on range safety;

- instructions on the care and cleaning of restricted firearms;

- examples of factors leading to firearm incidents and the misuse of firearms;

- a summary of ethics and laws affecting firearm owners and users;

- information on how to store, display, transport and handle restricted firearms safely;

- a glossary of firearm terms; and

- appendices

This is an introductory course. More information and training are available on the various shooting sports from their own qualified instructors, associations and local clubs. We recommend you contact them directly for further details.

Do not hesitate to contact provincial/territorial or local authorities for more detailed information on firearms laws and regulations in your area.

The Vital Four ACTS of Firearm Safety

Your instructor will refer to many different safety rules and guidelines. Time and again, the instructor will return to four basic rules. Any time you hear of an incident occurring, you can be sure at least one of these rules has been broken. These rules are known as the **Vital Four ACTS**.

The first letter of each rule becomes a letter in the acronym **ACTS.** You may want to think of these rules as acts you must carry out.

The Vital Four ACTS of Firearm Safety	
👉	**Assume every firearm is loaded.** • Regard any firearm as a potential danger.
👉	**Control the muzzle direction at all times.** • Identify the safest available muzzle direction. • Keep the firearm pointed in the safest available direction. • The muzzle of a firearm should not be pointed towards yourself or any other person.
👉	**Trigger finger must be kept off the trigger and out of the trigger guard.** • Do **NOT** put your finger on the trigger or inside the trigger guard when you pick up a firearm.
👉	**S**ee that the firearm is unloaded—PROVE it safe. • Do not handle the firearm unless you can properly **PROVE it safe**. • Check to see that both chamber and magazine are empty. Do this every time you handle a firearm, for any reason. • Pass or accept only open and unloaded firearms. It is an essential rule to adopt.

PROVE it safe

	Point the firearm in the safest available direction.
	Remove all ammunition.
	Observe the chamber(s).
	Verify the feeding path.
	Examine the bore for obstructions.

Legal Responsibilities

As a firearm owner and user, you have legal as well as social responsibilities. These responsibilities are laid out in federal, provincial/territorial and municipal laws and regulations. The table below describes a few of the regulations that come from each level of government.

Table 9. Some Legal Responsibilities of Restricted Firearm Owners/Users

Government Level	Example of Law or Regulation
Federal (e.g., *Firearms Act* and its Regulations, *Criminal Code*)	• All firearm owners need a valid firearms licence. • If you are the holder of a valid firearms licence and you own restricted firearms, you must inform the RCMP/CFP **before** you change your address and request an Authorization to Transport your restricted firearms. • Persons holding a valid PAL may borrow, buy, inherit or otherwise acquire the same class of firearm that he/she is licensed to own.
Provincial/Territorial (e.g., *Game, Fish and Wildlife Acts*)	• It is forbidden to hunt with a restricted firearm in Canada.
Municipal/County/Local (e.g., Noise, Nuisance, Zoning, By-laws)	• Some municipalities or counties may not allow the discharge of a firearm under any circumstances within their boundaries.

Other Duties of Firearm Owners/Users

a. A firearm owner/user must also keep informed about the laws and regulations affecting the use of firearms and ammunition.

b. Going beyond what the regulations require will increase your safety. Some suggestions are listed below:

- Keep an inventory of your firearms. Also keep any supporting documents such as photographs and owner's manuals. Store these documents in a safe place. This will help you describe any firearms that may be stolen or lost. It will also be easier for you to find your owner's manual and records of service or repair.

- Keep informed. Changes may occur in laws and regulations from time to time. This can happen whether at the federal, provincial/territorial or municipal level.

- Avoid advertising about the firearms in your home. You may be inviting theft.

 Every person commits an offence who, without lawful excuse, points a firearm at another person, whether the firearm is loaded or unloaded, and is:

1. **guilty of an indictable offence and liable to imprisonment for a term not exceeding five years; or**

2. **guilty of an offence punishable on summary conviction (a fine of $5,000 and/or six months imprisonment).**

Reference: Subsections 87(1) and (2) of Part III of the *Criminal Code*

They may also lose their firearm, lose their licence, receive a fine, receive jail time and/or be prohibited from possessing a firearm for a period of time.

Not all firearms laws are included in this Handbook. If you have any doubts about the regulations, or if you need more information, contact the following:

- The RCMP website: www.rcmp-grc.gc.ca/cfp
- CFP at 1-800-731-4000

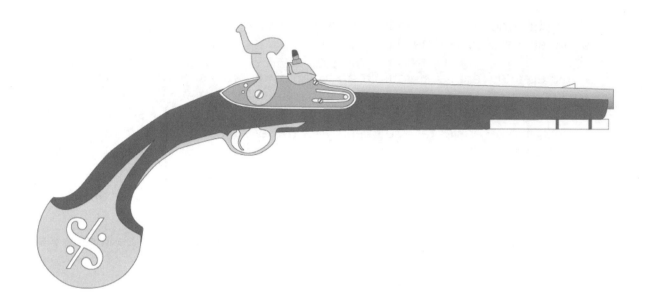

MODULE 12:

RESTRICTED FIREARMS MUZZLELOADER

MODULE 12: RESTRICTED FIREARMS MUZZLELOADER

12.1. Black powder and projectiles

12.1.1. Black powder

a. Muzzleloading firearms use black powder and lead balls as ammunition. There are also black powder substitutes.

b. Black powder is available in four different types.

Table 10. Types of Black Powder

Fg	Very coarse granules of powder. Used in larger bore muskets.
FFg	Finer granules than the Fg. Used in muzzleloading shotguns, big-bore rifles and single-shot pistols of .45 calibre and up.
FFFg	Finer granules than the FFg and the most common type. Used in nearly all cap and ball revolvers.
FFFFg	The finest granules. Used only in priming pans. **Never use this powder as powder charge**.

c. Remember, the finer the granules of powder, the more pressure it creates when fired.

d. Black powder ignites very easily. A glowing coal, a spark, even static electricity or a sharp blow may ignite it. Handle black powder with great care, especially when transporting it. Black powder should be stored in a secure, cool dry place and always in its original container.

e. As black powder ages, it becomes more unstable. When stored for long periods, the granules will begin to cake together and white crystals will form. When this happens, the black powder has become very unstable. It should be soaked immediately in water.

⚠ Never use FFFFg powder as anything other than a priming powder. Black powder ignites easily. Always handle with extreme care and wear eye protection. Never have a source of ignition around powder. Never smoke near black powder. Glowing embers may be present in the bore after firing a black-powder firearm. An explosion hazard could be created if you proceed immediately to reload. Never interchange smokeless powder and black powder. Use them only in firearms intended for their use.

12.1.2 Black powder projectiles

Modern black powder or muzzleloading firearms shoot several different types of projectiles as follows:

- Spherical/round ball, usually loaded along with a lubricated patch, which seals the barrel around the ball.

- Conical/cylindrical-shaped projectiles known as Mini-Balls, they have a hollow base that expands to seal the gases when the firearm fires.

- Shot/pellets of assorted sizes and materials.

- Sabot/plastic or synthetic carrier that encases a projectile.

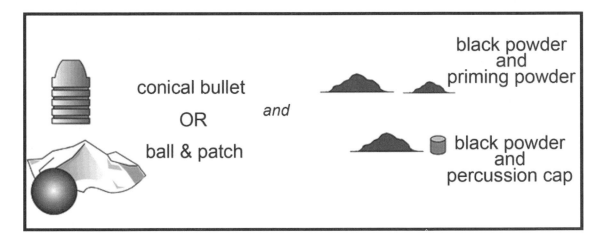

Figure 86. Ammunition Components for a Muzzleloader

12.2. Muzzleloading firearms

12.2.0. Overview

a. Muzzleloading handguns are still in use today. However, most modern muzzleloaders are reproductions of older designs.

b. This type of firearm is loaded through the muzzle. A measured amount of powder with a volumetric measure is poured through the muzzle into the barrel, followed by a patch, and finally a lead ball or shot. A hole located at the rear of the barrel just above the trigger allows a flash or spark to enter the barrel through the priming port and ignite the powder, firing the charge.

c. With flintlock muzzleloaders, the igniting spark is the result of the flint, held by the cock, hitting the frizzen. On percussion muzzleloaders, the flash is produced by the hammer striking a percussion cap.

d. Muzzleloading firearms use black powder or black powder substitutes. Black powder is classified as an explosive and is easily ignited by heat, friction, static electricity or a sharp blow and must be handled with extreme care. It is strongly recommended that individuals interested in muzzleloading seek additional training from qualified specialists in the field.

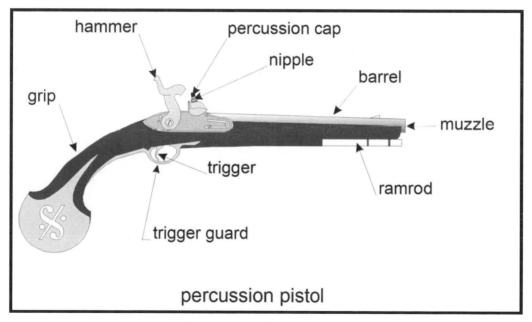

Figure 87. Muzzleloader

⚠ **Older firearms should be inspected by a qualified gunsmith to be sure they can be fired safely.**

12.2.1. Loading muzzleloaders

a. Today most firearms for black powder use are reproductions of muzzleloaders. Older firearms may not be safe to fire and should be checked by a gunsmith before use.

b. If a muzzleloader is not primed to fire, it is safer to handle. To ensure that a muzzleloader is not primed to fire, do the following:

1. Point the muzzle in the safest available direction and keep your finger off the trigger and out of the trigger guard.

2. Check that the hammer is not in full-cock position.

3. Check for the presence of priming powder in the percussion cap or in the priming pan.

4. If the firearm is primed, remove cap or priming powder.

c. In addition, it is difficult to tell if there is already a charge loaded into the barrel of a muzzleloader. Shooters should mark the firearm's ramrod at a level that shows the bore depth when the bore is empty (Figure 88). When the marked ramrod is inserted into the barrel, it shows whether or not the firearm is loaded.

⚠ **For other models of muzzleloading firearms, check with the manufacturer for specific safety features and information regarding the loading and unloading process.**

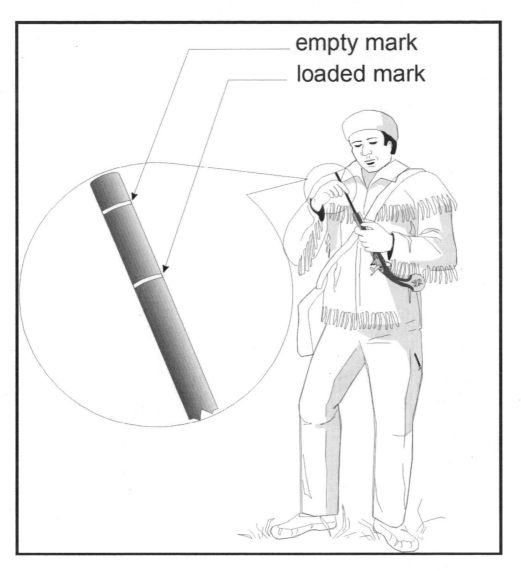

empty mark
loaded mark

Figure 88. Correctly Marked Ramrod

⚠ **It is very important that exact loading and unloading procedures are followed when handling muzzleloaders (Figure 89). Before attempting it, get the assistance of a qualified individual and carefully follow the instructions in your owner's manual. Ensure that the firing mechanism (lock) is rendered safe before proceeding to load the firearm. Before loading the firearm, use a rod with a tight fitting patch to clean the bore, and fire a cap to remove oil from the bore and flash port.**

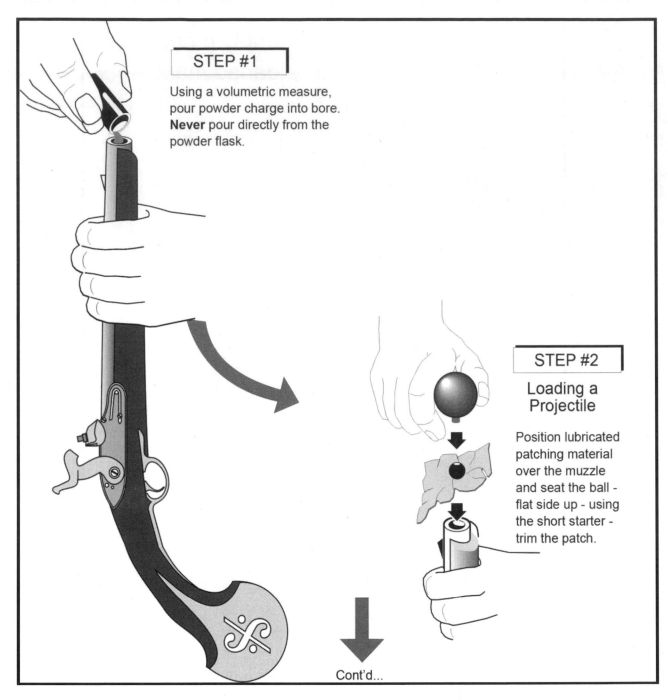

STEP #1

Using a volumetric measure, pour powder charge into bore. **Never** pour directly from the powder flask.

STEP #2

Loading a Projectile

Position lubricated patching material over the muzzle and seat the ball - flat side up - using the short starter - trim the patch.

Cont'd...

Figure 89. Loading a Muzzleloader

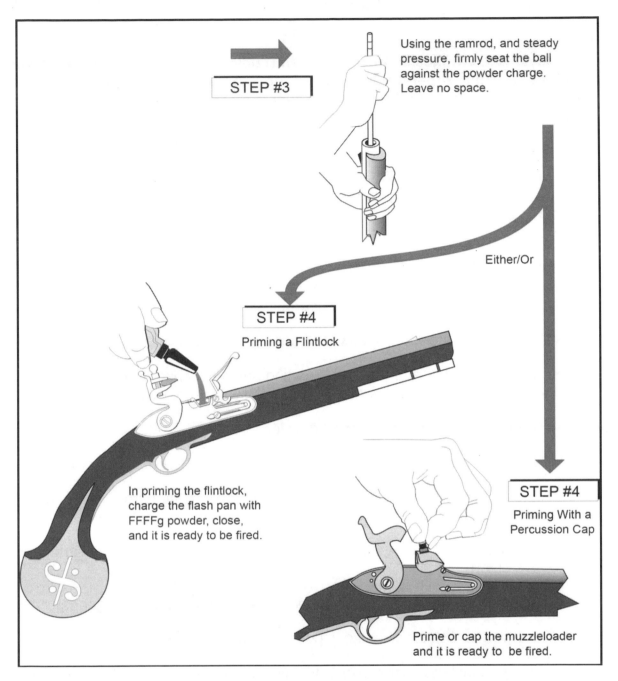

STEP #3

Using the ramrod, and steady pressure, firmly seat the ball against the powder charge. Leave no space.

Either/Or

STEP #4

Priming a Flintlock

In priming the flintlock, charge the flash pan with FFFFg powder, close, and it is ready to be fired.

STEP #4

Priming With a Percussion Cap

Prime or cap the muzzleloader and it is ready to be fired.

Figure 90. Loading a Muzzleloader *(cont'd)*

d. In black-powder revolvers, a measured amount of powder is poured into each chamber. A ball is firmly seated on each charge. Grease or lubricant is placed on top of each ball to lubricate its travel down the barrel and prevent "chain-firing" of all chambers. A percussion cap is put on the nipple of each chamber that produces the flash.

⚠ **Never use smokeless powder in a muzzleloader. Never use black powder in a modern cartridge firearm not designed for it. Always use a volumetric measure to put powder into the muzzle. Never pour directly from the main powder container. In compliance with firearms safe storage regulations, a muzzleloader with powder in the barrel is considered loaded.**

12.2.2. Cleaning a muzzleloader

a. A black-powder firearm must be properly cleaned after every firing session. Black powder is very corrosive. It attracts moisture, which causes rust.

b. Cleaning black-powder firearms improperly can result in carbon build-up in the barrel, which may cause coking. This condition may cause a glowing ember to remain after firing, resulting in a dangerous situation if the firearm is reloaded.

c. Use either commercial black powder cleaning solvent or hot, soapy water.

d. You will also need a ramrod with a cleaning patch attached. Use a rod as close to the bore diameter as possible. Refer to the owner's manual.

e. Use wet patches to soften the dried powder.

   1. Detach the barrel and place the lock end in a container of soapy water.

   2. Attach a patch to the ramrod. Insert the ramrod into the barrel. Pump the ramrod up and down until water flows from the top end of the barrel.

   3. Repeat step 2. Change the water as it becomes dirty. Repeat until the water stays clean.

   4. Dry the barrel out with several dry patches. Oil thoroughly with good gun oil.

   5. Remove the lock for cleaning, if possible, and oil after every use.

f. If cleaning a black-powder revolver, follow the manufacturer's instructions for the proper cleaning methods.

⚠ **It is strongly recommended that persons interested in muzzleloading seek additional training from experienced individuals.**

12.2.3. DOs and DON'Ts of muzzleloading

- Do have old muzzleloading firearms dismantled, examined and declared safe by a qualified gunsmith before using them.

- Do handle the muzzleloader with the same respect due all firearms.

- Do use ONLY black powder or black powder substitutes (e.g., Pyrodex) in your muzzleloader, never use smokeless powder.

- Do keep black powder far away from all cigarettes, matches/wicks or anything with an open flame, embers or anything that may cause sparks or heat.

- Do always use a volumetric measure to pour powder directly into the muzzle. Never use the powder horn or flask.

- Do carefully follow the manufacturer's recommendations for maximum powder charge.

- Do mark your ramrod to indicate when the barrel is empty and when it is loaded.

- Do wipe the bore clean of oil and excess grease before you load.

- Do make sure the ball or bullet is seated firmly on the powder charge.

- Do place grease in front of each projectile in a black-powder revolver to prevent chain-firing.

- Do treat a misfire as a hangfire that could fire at any second. Wait at least 60 seconds with the firearm pointed in a safe direction.

- Do wear safety glasses and hearing protection.

- Do reseat your second charge after firing and reloading a single barrel on a multiple-barrel black-powder firearm. Recoil can move the charge forward.

- Don't carry or handle a muzzleloading firearm with the hammer at full cock and primed unless you are ready to fire.

- Don't lean over or stand in front of the muzzle at any time.

- Don't load one chamber of a muzzleloading multiple barrel or revolving handgun unless the percussion caps on the nipples of the other barrels or chambers have been removed.

- Don't store a muzzleloader with powder in it.

Black powder is also used in some metallic cartridges for firearms specifically designed for their use. Care should be taken. Although they have the same name as a modern smokeless cartridge, they may not be interchangeable. Never interchange smokeless powder and black powder. Use them only in firearms intended for their use.

12.3. Review questions

1. Name two types of ammunition used in muzzleloading pistols.

2. List four sources that could cause black powder to ignite.

3. Before attempting to load a muzzleloading pistol, what safety consideration is given to the firing mechanism?

4. Use a cleaning agent on your firearm after every firing session of a black-powder muzzleloader. What are two possible choices of cleaning agents?

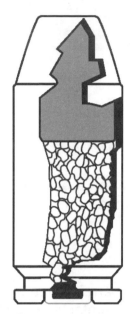

MODULE 13:

RESTRICTED FIREARMS AMMUNITION

MODULE 13: RESTRICTED FIREARMS AMMUNITION

13.0. Overview

This module discusses handgun cartridges.

⚠ **For more detailed information, consult a firearms dealer or a gunsmith. You can also consult the owner's manual.**

13.1. Rifling

a. Most hand guns have a rifled barrel. Rifled barrels have a series of spiral grooves inside the barrel. The ridges of metal between the grooves are called lands. The lands and grooves together make up the rifling (Figure 91).

b. Rifling makes the bullet spin as it leaves the barrel so that it will be stable in flight.

13.2. Calibre

a. Rifled firearms are sized by calibre. A calibre is a measurement of bore diameter in either thousands of an inch (Imperial) or in millimetres (Metric). Inch dimensions are usually measured from land to land, while metric dimensions are measured from groove to groove.

⚠ **Always consult the data stamp on the barrel of your firearm to find out the exact name of the ammunition that fits it.**

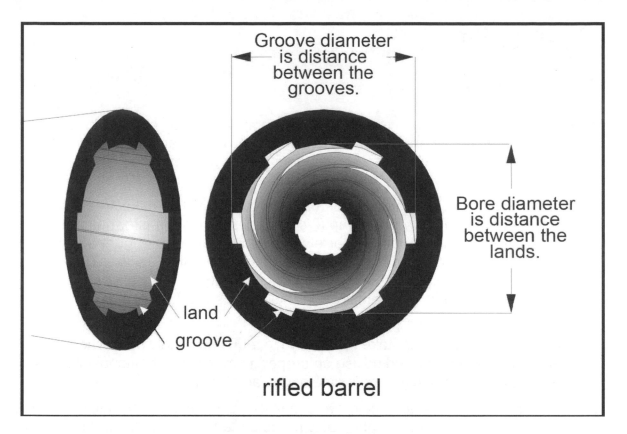

Figure 91. Rifled Barrel

13.3. Cartridges

13.3.0. Overview

a. A cartridge is the ammunition used in a firearm. Two kinds of cartridges commonly available are: rim-fire and centre-fire. These terms describe where the primer is located at the base of the cartridge casing. They also describe where the firing pin strikes.

b. Manufacturers produce firearms of many calibres. Always make sure that the cartridge name on the head stamp (Figure 92) matches the information on the data stamp, if available, on the barrel or slide of the firearm (Figure 93). This is the most important point to remember when selecting ammunition. Then choose the right type of ammunition for your firearm and target. The right shape or weight of the bullet is an example. If in doubt, consult a firearms or ammunition dealer.

c. If there is no data stamp, take the firearm to a qualified individual. They can measure the chamber and advise on proper ammunition. Additional information is available from manufacturer's catalogues and brochures.

d. Many firearm owners load their own centre-fire ammunition. This allows them to save money and create a high-quality product made specifically for their firearm and shooting conditions.

e. Incorrectly loaded ammunition may cause the firearm to malfunction or jam. Malfunctions could lead to an incident. The firearm could blow up and injure the shooter. Do not accept or use reloaded cartridges unless you know that they were made and reloaded correctly.

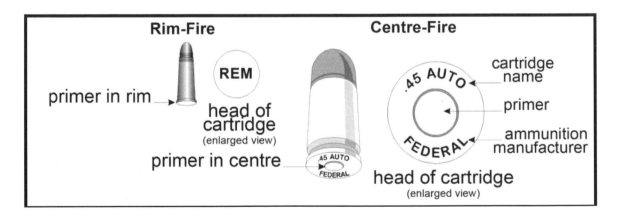

Figure 92. Example of a Rim-fire and Centre-fire Cartridge with Head Stamp

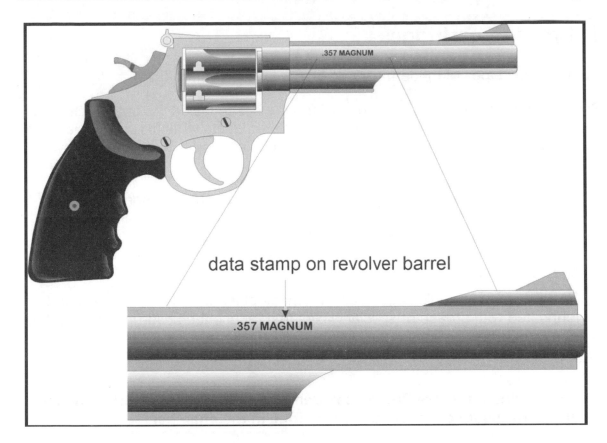

Figure 93. Example of a Barrel Data Stamp

Some firearms may not have a data stamp, or they may have an incorrect stamp. Some firearms may have been altered and the existing data stamp may be incorrect. They should be checked by a qualified individual before use. If you are reloading your own ammunition, you must strictly follow the instructions and procedures outlined in the manuals provided for this process. Visually inspect all cartridge components for defects before loading.

13.3.1. Types of cartridges

There are two basic types of modern cartridges: rim-fire and centre-fire.

a. Rim-fire ammunition's priming chemical fills the space inside the bottom rim of a thin brass or copper cartridge casing. The soft rim dents when struck by the firing pin. This crushes the priming compound. It explodes, and this ignites the powder (Figure 94).

- The .17hmr is also a rim-fire ammunition but the popular modern rim-fire cartridges are .22 calibre. They commonly come in short, long and long rifle. A .22-magnum cartridge is also available; however, it is not interchangeable with the other .22 cartridges. Be sure to use the correct ammunition for your specific firearm.

- Rim-fire cartridge bullets generally are made of lead. They can be jacketed or lubricated with grease or special waxes that reduce the build-up of lead in the handgun barrel except for the .17hmr that is jacketed.

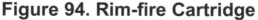 **Dry firing a rim-fire firearm can damage the firearm. Dry firing means to initiate a firing sequence without a cartridge in the chamber.**

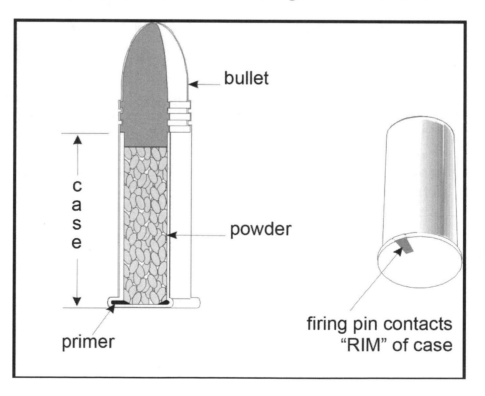

Figure 94. Rim-fire Cartridge

b. Centre-fire ammunition is generally used for larger more powerful calibre firearms. The primer is located at the centre of the base of the cartridge case. The firing pin strikes the primer. This explodes the priming compound. This in turn ignites the powder charge.

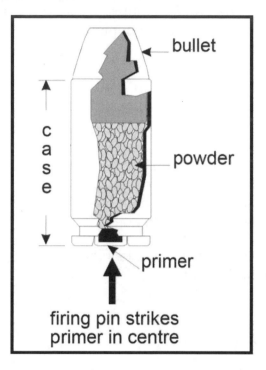

Figure 95. Centre-fire Cartridge

Table 11. Sizes and Types of Handgun Ammunition

TYPE	COMPONENTS	PURPOSE
Sizes: calibre e.g., .22 or .45 or 9 mm **Figure 96. Rim-fire and Centre-fire**	**BULLET**	Strikes target
	POWDER	Burns and expands to propel bullet
	CASE	Contains components
	PRIMER	Fires powder charge when struck by firing pin

13.3.2. Cartridge names

a. There are various ways of identifying or "naming" cartridges. Some cartridges have several names. The cartridge name, or an abbreviation of it, is stamped on the head of the case. It is also found printed on the ammunition manufacturer's box.

⚠️ **Cartridges with different names are not interchangeable (such as .38 S&W/.38 Special/.38 Super Auto)**

b. A manufacturer may choose to make a firearm or ammunition in a cartridge originally made by another manufacturer, and as a result, confusion can occur. For example, you can use a Remington rifle to fire a .300 Winchester Magnum cartridge made by the Federal Cartridge Company.

c. The head stamp includes very valuable information, such as the cartridge name. It may also tell you the following:

- the caliber;

- the manufacturer; and

- whether the ammunition is regular or magnum and any other relevant details.

d. Always read the cartridge name. It is the only way to be sure that the cartridge matches the firearm. If in doubt, check with a gunsmith or gun shop.

e. The term magnum comes from the description of a large bottle of wine. It was first applied to large bottleneck cartridges that produced greater power than was the normal standard for that calibre. Today, it is more a marketing term than a technical term, but it is an important part of the name.

f. To choose the right ammunition for the type of target and firearm, follow the manufacturer's recommendations. For handgun ammunition, the manufacturer's recommendations are included in the catalogues distributed through sporting goods stores and gun shops.

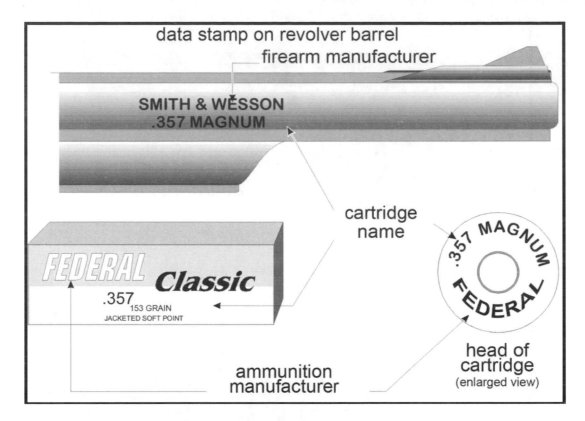

Figure 97. Cartridge Head Stamp, Data Stamp and Ammunition Box Label

⚠️ Some ammunition may not have a cartridge name stamp, such as rim-fire cartridges. Refer to the information on the ammunition box. If in doubt, have any such ammunition checked by a qualified individual before you use it.

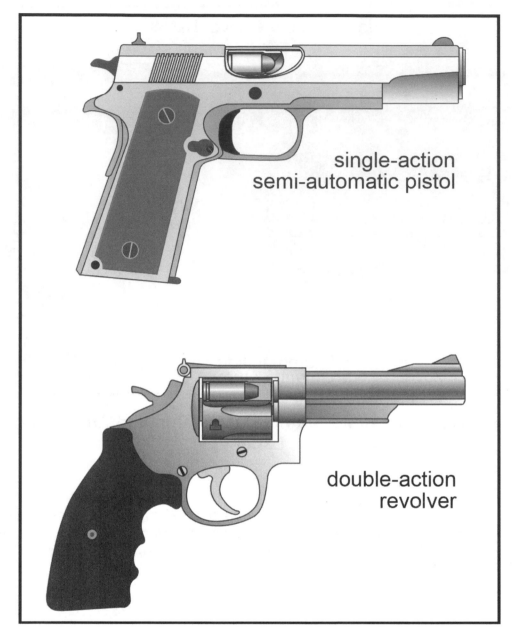

Figure 98. Chambered Ammunition Cut-away

13.3.3. Cartridge components and materials

Ammunition varies in size, appearance and materials. Ammunition cartridges for handguns are made up of the four basic components described below (Figures 99 and 100):

1. The bullet is the projectile at the front end of the cartridge. It is propelled from the firearm by the expansion or explosion of gas from the burning powder. Usually, the bullet is made of lead, lead alloy or other dense material. It may also be covered by a jacket of a harder metal. When the nose of the bullet is covered in this manner, it may be referred to as a full-metal jacket, hard point or ball ammunition. If the lead is exposed at the front of the bullet, it is referred to as a jacketed soft point. Copper or gilding metal is commonly used as jacket materials. Bullets come in a variety of sizes, shapes and weights. You must select the right combination for the target that you plan to shoot. Target bullets are often made from lead alloy. Lead handgun target bullets are commonly of a design known as a wadcutter or semi-wadcutter. Their sharp edges produce precise holes in paper targets.

2. The powder charge is a chemical compound inside the case. It is ignited to propel the bullet through the barrel.

3. The case holds all the other ammunition parts. It is usually made of brass. It could also be made of steel, copper or aluminum.

4. The primer contains a chemical mixture that explodes when the firing pin strikes it. This explosion ignites the powder charge.

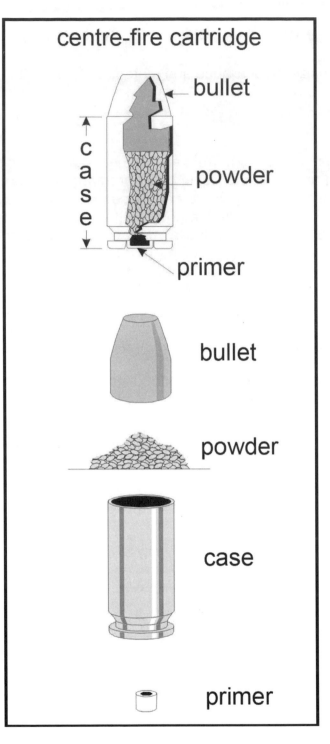

Figure 99. Centre-fire Bullet, Powder Charge, Case and Primer

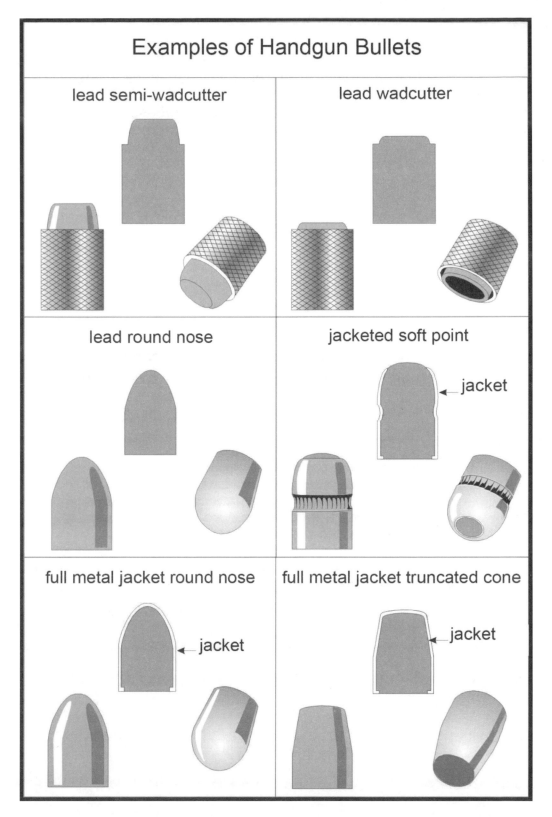

Figure 100. Examples of Handgun Bullets

13.4. Ballistics

a. Ballistics is the study of projectiles in flight and what affects them.

b. Modern firearms can shoot a long distance. For this reason, every shooter should understand ballistics. Handguns can shoot a bullet more than two kilometres.

c. Ballistics tables for ammunition supply the information to calculate the flight path and performance of cartridges.

d. You want to shoot safely. Therefore, you need to know how far your projectile will travel. That means that you need to know the dangerous range.

⚠ **Be sure of your target and beyond. If there is any reason your shot may be unsafe, do not fire.**

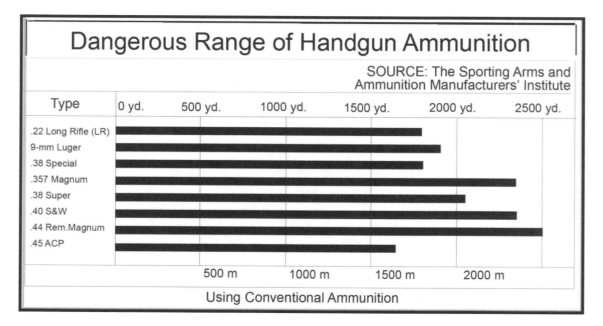

Figure 101. Dangerous Range of Handgun Ammunition

13.5. Trajectory

a. The trajectory is the path a discharged shot or bullet takes during flight. Several factors affect this path; examples include, but are not limited to, the following:

- Gravity pulls the bullet down toward the ground as it is travelling forward. This results in a downward curved path.

- Air resistance slows down the flight of the bullet.

- Velocity is the speed at which a bullet travels in a given time and direction.

- Mass is the weight of the bullet.

b. The firearm muzzle must be raised from the horizontal position to make up for gravity. The trajectory of a projectile is curved. It crosses the line of sight twice on the way to a target.

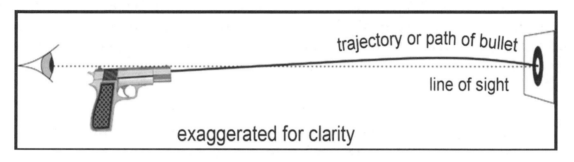

Figure 102. Trajectory of a Bullet

Responsible shooters will follow the recommendations below:

- **Shoot only at targets within effective range.**

- **Consider the maximum distance the shot or bullet may travel beyond the target.**

- **You are responsible for where the bullet stops.**

13.6. Hazards

The selection of the correct ammunition for the firearm is critical to safe operation but sometimes even the correct cartridge can fail to fire properly. Modern commercial ammunition is normally very reliable but there are several ways the cartridge may not fire.

- A misfire is a cartridge that does not fire. Misfired cartridges should not be reused in the firearm and must be disposed of properly. Muzzleloading firearms may also misfire.

- A hangfire is a delayed fire in which the firing pin strikes the primer but it does not create enough flame to ignite the powder instantly. If the muzzle is not pointed in a safe direction when the cartridge eventually fires, it may result in an injury. If the cartridge is removed from the chamber and then discharges, the explosive rupture of the case may also cause injury. Muzzleloading firearms may also have a hangfire.

- A primer pop (squib load) happens when the cartridge does not contain any gunpowder or when the gunpowder is no longer effective. The firearm will discharge the primer without the usual noise or recoil. This may have enough force to push the bullet out of the case, but the bullet may lodge in the barrel. If another bullet is fired, the barrel may rupture and cause possible injury.

If the trigger is pulled and there is no noticeable discharge, wait 60 seconds while pointing the muzzle in a safe direction. If there is no hangfire within 60 seconds, open the action and unload the firearm. PROVE the firearm safe to ensure that there are no bullets lodged in the barrel.

13.7. Firearm malfunctions

Generally, using commercially made ammunition and a properly maintained firearm, malfunctions will not occur. Firearms jammed with a cartridge in the chamber(s) can be hazardous. This hazard, if not dealt with properly, may result in a serious injury. Consult a qualified person or gunsmith for information on how to perform this function in the safest possible manner with your particular firearm.

13.8. Ammunition precautions and legislation

Explosives information is issued by Natural Resources Canada. It indicates that you may keep reasonable quantities of sporting ammunition on your property. "Reasonable" means quantities typically required for a rifle, handgun, shotgun or for part of a collection. This ammunition must be for your private use, not resale. Contact Natural Resources Canada for details. You must take every necessary precaution against incidents by adhering to the instructions below:

- Ammunition must be stored out of children's reach. It must be kept away from flammables.

- Ammunition for a restricted firearm may only be stored in a place where it is not within easy access to the firearm, unless the ammunition is stored, together with or separately from the firearm in:

  o a securely locked container or receptacle that cannot be easily broken open or into; or

  o a securely locked vault, safe or room specifically built or adapted for the secure storage of restricted firearms.

- In a dwelling house, ammunition for a restricted firearm must not be displayed with the firearm and it cannot be within easy access to the firearm from which it can be discharged.

- In a place other than a dwelling house, ammunition for a restricted firearm must not be displayed with the firearm and it cannot be within easy access to the firearm from which it can be discharged, unless the ammunition is displayed in a securely locked container or receptacle that cannot be easily broken open or into.

- All ammunition should be stored in a cool, dry place, preferably in a vented container. This will reduce the chance of corrosion or breakdown of ammunition components that could cause the firearm to jam or misfire.

Keep in mind that storing ammunition in an unvented container may create an explosive hazard during a fire.

Ammunition Safety Points to Remember

- Carry ammunition only for the firearm you are using.

- Never experiment with unfamiliar ammunition.

- Using modern ammunition in old firearms may be hazardous.

- When a misfire occurs, slowly count to 60 while pointing the muzzle in a safe direction. Remove the cartridge following safe procedures. Then, carefully inspect the bore for obstructions.

- Never use old or corroded ammunition or reloading components.

- Never use cartridges if you are uncertain about their safe use.

- Never interchange smokeless powder and black powder. Use them only in firearms intended for their use.

- Store all ammunition so that unauthorized persons do not have access to it.

- Ammunition should never be displayed with a firearm.

- Ammunition is most safely carried in its original container.

- When hand loading your own ammunition, be certain to strictly follow the procedures in the manuals about reloading ammunition. Treat primers with extra caution—they are explosive devices.

13.9. Review questions

1. What are the spiral grooves cut inside the barrel called?

2. Name the two basic types of modern ammunition.

3. How do you identify the calibre of ammunition cartridges?

4. How long should you wait after a misfire, before you ACTS/PROVE your firearm?

5. Is it safe to use a .357 cartridge in a firearm chambered for a .38 special?

MODULE 14:

OPERATING HANDGUN ACTIONS

MODULE 14: OPERATING HANDGUN ACTIONS

14.0. Overview

a. To understand the safe use of firearms, you must become familiar with action types, how they work, and how to safely load and unload them.

b. This module first defines the different types of firearms, various safeties and action releases and shows how to do the following:

- identify each type of action;

- locate safeties (some actions will not open unless the safety is **OFF**);

- open actions and unload—**ACTS and PROVE it safe**; and

- safely load each type of action, with the safety **ON**, whenever possible.

Always wear safety glasses and hearing protection when loading and discharging firearms.

14.1. Common types of handgun actions

Handguns are generally classified by their type of action. There are two basic types as follows:

a. A revolving action is used for some handguns. It has several chambers in a rotating cylinder and can contain one cartridge in each chamber. Revolvers are manufactured as a non-swing cylinder, a swing-out cylinder or a top break.

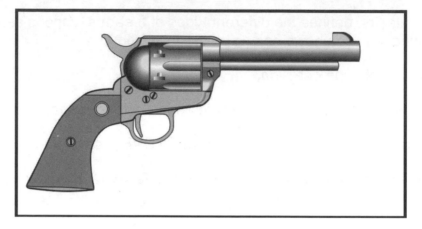

Figure 103. Revolver

b. A semi-automatic action extracts and ejects empty casings and inserts another cartridge in the chamber automatically after each pull of the trigger.

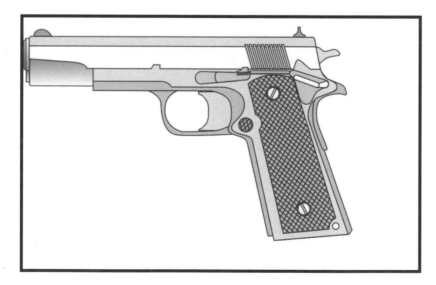

Figure 104. Semi-automatic

14.2. Other types of handgun actions

a. A hinge (or break) action opens near the breech and is usually single barrel.

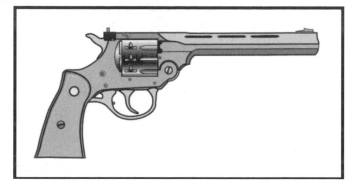

Figure 105. Break-action Revolver

b. A bolt action is similar to those found on long guns and can be either single shot or multiple shot.

14.3. Trigger functions

There are three primary functions. They are single action only, single and double action and double action only.

a. A single action is an action that releases the hammer from a cocked position when the trigger is pulled.

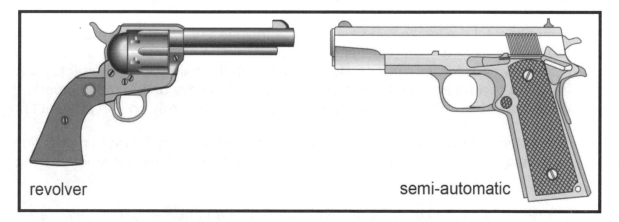

revolver   semi-automatic

Figure 106. Single-action Handguns

b. A single and double action is an action that cocks and fires with a complete pull of the trigger. Double actions may also fire in single action mode.

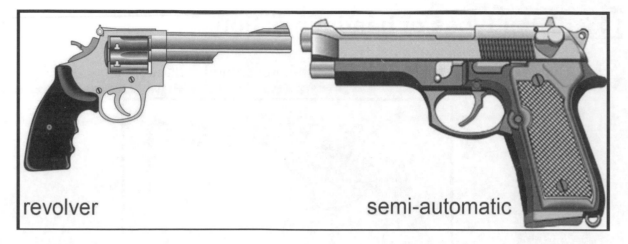

Figure 107. Double-action Handguns

c. A double action only is an action that cannot fire in the single action mode.

⚠ **Double action / single action requires a different trigger pull between the first and subsequent shots.**

14.4. Safeties

14.4.0. Overview

a. A mechanical device known as a safety is included on most firearms to reduce the chances of unintentional firing. However, mechanical devices can fail. A hard blow may cause some firearms to fire even with the safety ON. Therefore, safe handling of a firearm by the person holding it will always be the most important firearm safety device. Always use the safety, but never rely on it to prevent firing.

b. The safety is designed to prevent the firearm from firing by interrupting the firing sequence. The safety blocks one or more of the trigger, sear, hammer or firing pin.

c. There are two types of safeties: manual safeties and built-in safety devices. Manual safeties can be placed on or off. They include slide safeties, like the lever safety, and frame safeties, like the safety lock. Built-in safety devices may prevent unintentional discharge. They include decocking levers, trigger safeties, magazine disconnects and grip safeties.

Never rely on a safety to prevent unintentional firing. A safety can fail. All safeties are slightly different. Consult the owner's manual. Different manufacturers may use different terminology to describe their safeties.

14.4.1. Manual safeties

a. The lever safety is found on either the right or left side of the receiver. It is operated by pushing forward and back to either the ON or OFF position.

b. The safety lock is normally operated by pushing it up into a notch on the slide. These safeties are commonly found on the left side of the receiver, near the hammer on single-action semi-automatics.

c. With semi-automatic handguns, the hammer is automatically placed into the full-cock position each time the slide is pulled to the rear. In single and double-action semi-automatic handguns, the hammer remains in this position. In double action only, the hammer returns forward to the rest position. Whenever possible, when operating the action of any firearm, always have the safety on.

14.4.2. Built-in safeties

These safety devices may or may not be present on your firearm. Always consult your owner's manual.

a. With a double-action semi-automatic handgun, there may be a decocking device or decocking lever. These are common on modern models. Instead of carefully manually decocking the hammer as you would with single-action revolvers and semi-automatics, you need only depress the decocking lever. The decocking lever safely lowers the hammer. To accomplish this task, hold the firearm firmly in the strong hand and depress the decocking lever with the weak hand thumb. On some handguns, the decocking lever also engages the safety. Double-action-only handguns do not have a decocking lever.

b. The trigger safety is found on some models of handguns. This is a pivoting device found as a part of the trigger. As the trigger is pulled, the safety moves to the OFF position and the handgun can be fired.

c. The magazine disconnect safety prevents the firearm from being discharged when the magazine is removed.

d. The grip safety is usually found on semi-automatic handguns. It disengages when the firearm is held in and ready to fire.

e. The hammer block / transfer bar will prevent the firing pin from touching the primer. On many older revolvers, the firing pin may rest on the primer of any cartridges directly below it when the hammer is in the forward position. If the hammer is struck, the cartridge will fire. Most modern revolvers include a safety device to prevent this from happening. This is normally accomplished by preventing the firing pin from touching the primer unless the trigger is held all the way to the rear. The most common safety devices used to accomplish this are the hammer block and transfer bar. Consult your owner's manual or a gunsmith to find out if your revolver has one of these devices.

> **! Be very careful when moving the hammer. It could slip from beneath your weak hand thumb and fire the cartridge. Persons who are right handed would consider their left hand as their weak hand. The presence of a half cock on a firearm does not guarantee it is a safety. Some firearms do not use it as a safety. Consult the owner's manual.**

f. Safely lowering the hammer from the full-cock position on a single-action revolver requires caution. The following method can be used when a "cease-fire" is called and the hammer is at full cock:

1. While maintaining a solid grip with the strong hand, place the weak-hand thumb fully on the hammer.

2. Pull the trigger with the strong-hand finger and begin to slowly lower the hammer fully forward. When the hammer is disengaged, release the trigger. If a semi-cocked position exists on the firearm, the hammer will immediately stop.

g. There are some differences between various models of single-action handguns. If possible with the model you are using, move the trigger finger off the trigger and out of the trigger guard immediately after the hammer begins to move forward. Slowly and carefully lower the hammer. If there is no half-cock position, lower the hammer all the way forward and down.

h. Double-action handguns also rely on a heavy double-action trigger pull as a further safety barrier to unintentional firing.

⚠ **Before loading any firearm, determine the position of the safety. Although all the illustrations of revolvers and pistols in this manual depict firearms with exposed hammers, many manufacturers produce them with internal hammers. Although some of these internal hammers function identically to the external hammers on comparable pistols, most function more like the mechanism on a bolt action. The hammer does not pivot on an axis; it moves back and forth in a straight line. It is called a striker. Some striker mechanisms use a built-in firing pin; others hit the firing pin and drive it forward. All the safety procedures for exposed hammers apply to internal hammers, but because the hammer is not visible, it is difficult to see if the hammer is cocked. Great care should be taken.**

14.5. Action releases

Most handguns, other than semi-automatics, have some type of mechanism that must be moved to allow an action to be opened or closed. The location of the action release mechanism depends on the make and model of the firearm.

⚠ **Do not touch any firearm unless you know how to handle it safely. If you do not know, consult the owner's manual or consult a gunsmith who knows that firearm well.**

14.6. General loading and unloading procedures

Before attempting to unload a firearm, first follow the **Vital Four ACTS of Firearm Safety** and **PROVE it safe**.

The Vital Four ACTS of Firearm Safety	
☞	**Assume every firearm is loaded.** • Regard any firearm as a potential danger.
☞	**Control the muzzle direction at all times.** • Identify the safest available muzzle direction. • Keep the firearm pointed in the safest available direction. • The muzzle of a firearm should not be pointed towards yourself or any other person.
☞	**Trigger finger must be kept off the trigger and out of the trigger guard.** • Do **NOT** put your finger on the trigger or inside the trigger guard when you pick up a firearm.
☞	**See that the firearm is unloaded—PROVE it safe.** • Do not handle the firearm unless you can properly **PROVE it safe**. • Check to see that both chamber and magazine are empty. Do this every time you handle a firearm, for any reason. • Pass or accept only open and unloaded firearms. It is an essential rule to adopt.

14.6.1. Unloading procedure: ACTS and PROVE it safe

PROVE is an acronym, or memory aid, that stands for the five steps required to ensure that a firearm is unloaded and is safe. The five steps are: Point, Remove, Observe, Verify and Examine. These procedures must be followed to safely unload any firearm.

1. **P**oint the firearm in the safest available direction throughout the unloading procedure.

   - Make sure that nothing touches the trigger throughout this procedure.

   - Put the safety **ON**, if it can be left on during the unloading process.

2. **R**emove all ammunition as follows:

   - If the firearm has a detachable magazine, remove the magazine from the firearm first (this prevents a semi-automatic from chambering another cartridge if the action closes).

   - Open the action to remove any cartridges from the chamber(s).

   - Leave the action open.

3. **O**bserve the chamber(s) to confirm that there is no cartridge(s) or empty casing(s).

4. **V**erify that the feeding path is clear of ammunition, casings or foreign objects.

5. **E**xamine the bore for lubricant, rust or other obstructions.

The firearm is now unloaded and safe until it leaves the direct control of the person who unloaded and **ACTS—PROVEd it safe**.

14.6.2. Checking the barrel for obstructions

Always check the barrel and chamber for obstructions before loading.

⚠ **Only load a firearm when you intend to use it, and only in an area where it can be safely and legally discharged.**

14.6.3. Loading procedure

1. Prepare the firearm for loading by going through the complete unloading procedure **ACTS—PROVE it safe**.

2. Clear any obstructions from the chamber(s) and bore(s). Clean if required.

3. Put the safety **ON**, if it can be left on during the loading process.

4. Point the firearm in the safest available direction throughout the loading and chambering procedure.

5. Make sure that nothing touches the trigger throughout this process.

6. Where possible, with the action open, select and load the correct ammunition by matching the data stamp on the firearm to the head stamp on the cartridge.

7. Point down range, extend arm, locking wrist and elbow, and close the action.

8. Leave any safety on (if applicable) until ready to fire.

The firearm is now loaded and ready for use. It requires continuous care and attention until it is unloaded.

Always be sure of your target and beyond.

14.6.4. Loading and unloading the most common action types

Do not attempt to handle any firearm that you are uncomfortable handling. To ensure safe handling of any firearm, seek the assistance of a qualified individual.

14.7. Operating repeating firearms: revolver actions

14.7.0. Overview

a. All firearms have their own unique aspects. One of the best ways to discover the specific methods for unloading and loading your particular firearm is to study the owner's manual. The steps outlined in this module are not meant to replace a full understanding of a given firearm owner's manual. The following information is an introduction to the most common actions. The general procedure does not change, but the details can vary significantly.

b. Many firearms are repeaters. Revolvers, for example, are repeaters because they hold more than one cartridge and can be fired several times in a row. The most common repeating handguns are the revolvers described in this module.

c. The extra cartridges in a manually repeating revolver are contained in the cylinder (Figure 108).

d. The revolving action takes its name from a revolving cylinder containing a number of cartridge chambers. One chamber at a time lines up with the barrel and hammer. Revolver cylinders may rotate either clockwise or counter-clockwise, depending on the manufacturer.

e. Most single-action revolvers have cylinders that are incapable of swinging out. Cartridges are inserted and removed one at a time through a loading port, usually located on the right side. When firing the single-action revolver, the hammer must be manually placed in the full-cock position for each shot. Pulling the trigger completes one function. It releases the hammer.

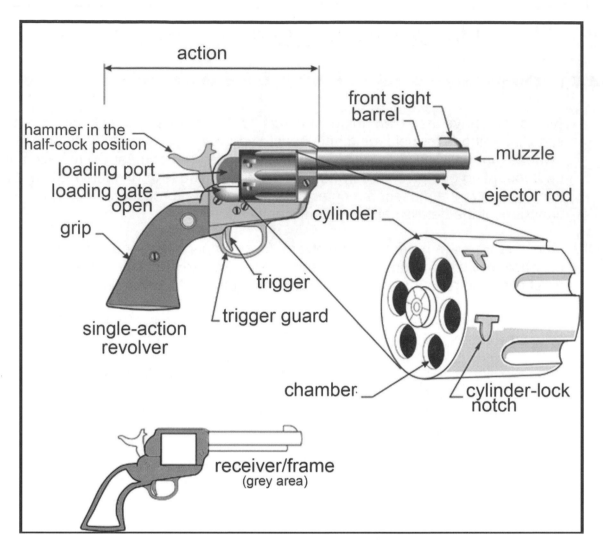

Figure 108. Single-action Revolver

14.7.1. Revolver: single-action non-swing-out cylinder (loading gate) / unloading procedure—ACTS and PROVE it safe

⚠️ **Before attempting to unload a firearm, first follow the Vital Four ACTS of Firearm Safety—PROVE it safe.**

1. **P**oint the firearm in the safest available direction throughout the unloading procedure.

   - Make sure that nothing touches the trigger throughout this procedure.

   - Open the loading gate and check if the cylinder will rotate. If the cylinder does NOT rotate, put the safety **ON**, hammer in half-cock/loading notch during the unloading procedure.

2. **R**emove all ammunition as follows:

   When the cylinder rotates, observe each chamber through the loading port, as you turn the cylinder, to ensure that there are no cartridges in the cylinder. If any cartridges or casings are present, use the ejector rod under the barrel to remove them. The chamber must be aligned with the loading port. Push the ejector rod from the front to the back. Let any cartridge or casing fall on the shooting bench or range floor and leave it there until you have completed all the steps.

3. **O**bserve every chamber(s) to confirm that there is no cartridge(s) or empty casing(s).

4. **V**erify by inspecting to ensure that the feeding path is clear of ammunition, casings or foreign objects.

5. **E**xamine the bore for lubricant, rust or other obstructions.

The firearm is now unloaded and safe until it leaves the direct control of the person who unloaded and ACTS—PROVEd it safe.

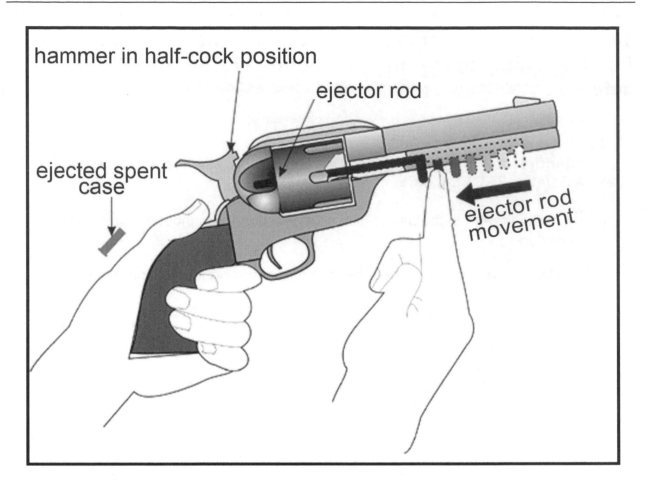

Figure 109. Removing a Cartridge from a Single-action Revolver

14.7.2. Revolver: single-action non-swing-out cylinder (loading gate) / loading procedure

⚠ Only load a firearm when you intend to use it, and only in an area where it can be safely and legally discharged.

1. Prepare the firearm for loading by going through the complete unloading procedure—**ACTS** and **PROVE it safe**.

2. Clear any obstructions from the chamber(s) and barrel. Clean if required.

3. Point the firearm in the safest available direction throughout the loading procedure.

4. Make sure that nothing touches the trigger throughout this process.

5. Put the safety **ON**, if applicable. While most revolvers do not have safeties, some do. Consult your owner's manual or ask a qualified gunsmith.

6. With the loading gate open, select the correct ammunition by matching the data stamp on the firearm with the head stamp on the cartridge. Insert the cartridge(s) into the chamber(s).

7. Close the loading gate covering the port.

8. Leave any safety on (if applicable) until ready to fire.

The firearm is now loaded and ready for use. It requires continuous attention until it is unloaded.

⚠ **Always be sure of your target and beyond.**

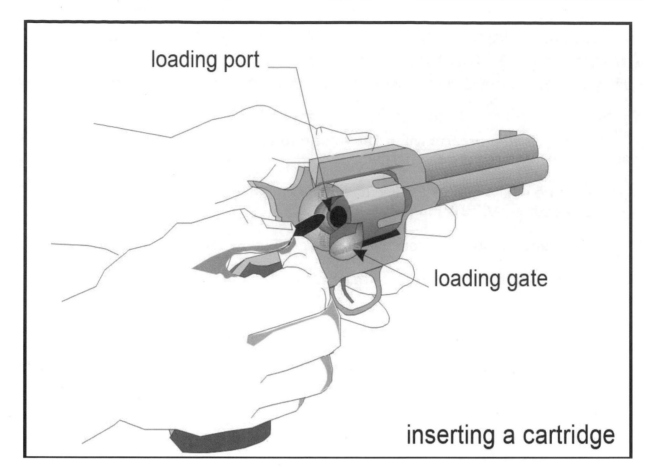

loading port

loading gate

inserting a cartridge

Figure 110. Loading a Single-action (loading gate revolver)

14.7.3. Revolver: double-action swing-out cylinder and break open / unloading procedure—ACTS and PROVE it safe

⚠ Before attempting to unload a firearm, first follow the Vital Four ACTS of Firearm Safety—PROVE it safe.

1. **P**oint the firearm in the safest available direction throughout the unloading procedure:

   • Make sure that nothing touches the trigger throughout this procedure.

   • Put the safety **ON**, if applicable. While most revolvers do not have safeties, some do. Consult your owner's manual or ask a qualified gunsmith.

2. **R**emove all ammunition as follows:

   • Operate the cylinder release and expose the chambers by swinging the cylinder to the side or top.

   • Tip the muzzle slightly upward in a safe direction and operate the ejector rod to allow the cartridges or empty casings to fall out. If not ejected, remove them by hand. Let any cartridge or casing fall on the shooting bench or range floor and leave it there until you have completed all the steps.

   • Leave the action open.

3. **O**bserve the chambers to confirm that there are no cartridges or empty casings.

4. **V**erify by inspecting to ensure that the feeding path is clear of ammunition, casings or foreign objects.

5. **E**xamine the bore for lubricant, rust or other obstructions.

The firearm is now unloaded and safe until it leaves the direct control of the person who unloaded and PROVEd it safe.

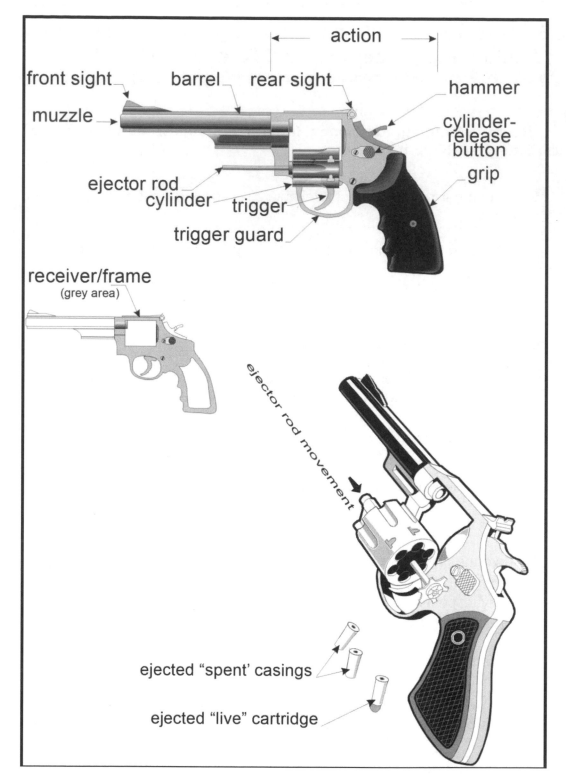

Figure 111. Double-action Revolver Swing-out Cylinder

In a double-action revolver, pulling the trigger all the way to the rear completes two functions:

1. turns the cylinder so a cartridge lines up with the barrel under the hammer; and

2. cocks and releases the hammer.

The cylinder normally has a release that enables it to swing out. This allows more than one cartridge at a time to be inserted, or ejected from, the cylinder.

14.7.4. Revolver: double-action break open / loading procedure—ACTS and PROVE it safe

Only load a firearm when you intend to use it and only in an area where it can be safely and legally discharged.

1. Prepare the firearm for loading by going through the complete unloading procedure—**ACTS and PROVE it safe**.

2. Clear any obstructions from the chamber(s) and bore. Clean if required.

3. Point the firearm in the safest available direction throughout the loading procedure.

4. Make sure that nothing touches the trigger throughout this process.

5. Leave the hammer fully down (if possible) during the loading process.

6. With the action open, select the correct ammunition by verifying that the data stamp on the firearm matches the head stamp on the cartridge.

7. Place the cartridge(s) into the chamber(s).

8. Close the cylinder firmly, locking the action closed.

9. Leave any safety **ON** and the hammer down, if applicable, until ready to fire.

The firearm is now loaded and ready for use. It requires continuous care and attention until it is unloaded.

⚠ Always be sure of your target and beyond.

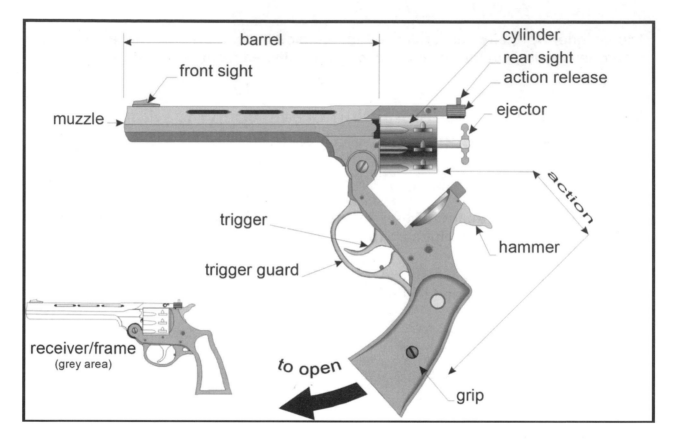

Figure 112. Top-break Revolver

⚠ Break-open revolvers operate in a similar manner to other double-action revolvers. Instead of the cylinder typically swinging out, the action hinges open, normally to the top or bottom.

14.8. Semi-automatic actions: pistols

14.8.0. Overview

a. With each pull of the trigger, the semi-automatic action uses part of the energy of the expanding gas from the burning powder to extract the empty cartridge case and to chamber the next cartridge. There is no need to load another cartridge into the firing position. Each time a cartridge is fired, the empty case is ejected and another cartridge is placed into the chamber from the magazine.

b. Semi-automatic handguns are further divided into single action, double action and double action only. In double action (D/A) and single action (S/A), the hammer stays cocked after each shot is fired, though the trigger pull is shorter and may need less pressure once the first shot is discharged. In D/A only, the hammer returns to the forward position after each shot is fired.

c. Semi-automatic safeties vary considerably. Most are located near the hammer. Consult your owner's manual or a qualified gunsmith.

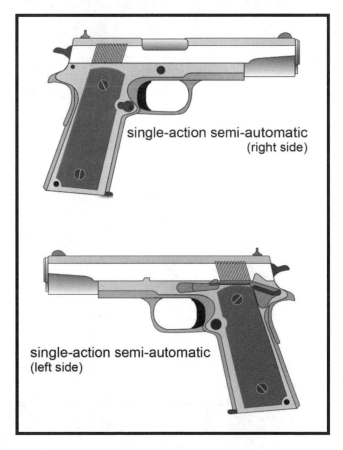

Figure 113. Single-action Semi-automatic

273

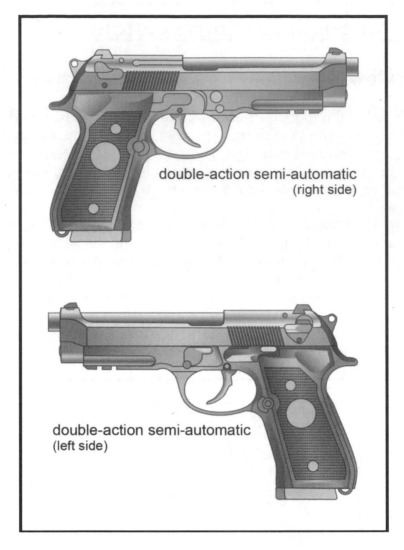

Figure 114. Single/double-action Semi-automatic

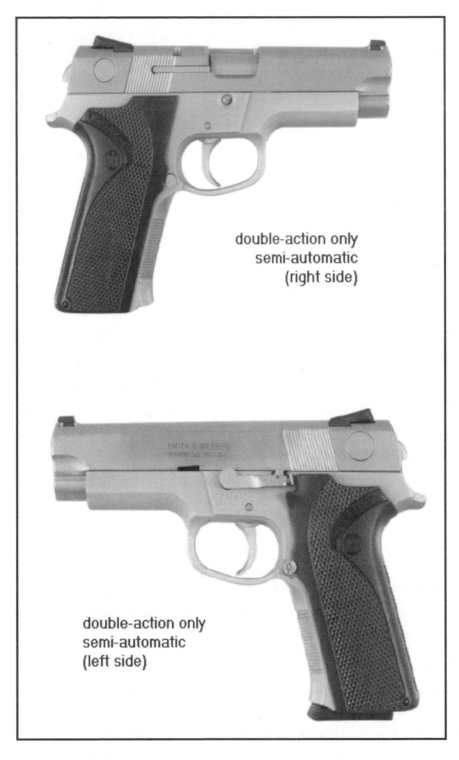

Figure 115. Double-action-only Semi-automatic

14.8.1. Semi-automatic: single action, single/double action, and double action only unloading procedure—ACTS and PROVE it safe

⚠️ **Before attempting to unload a firearm, first follow the Vital Four ACTS— PROVE it safe.**

1. **P**oint the firearm in the safest available direction throughout the unloading procedure:

    - Make sure that nothing touches the trigger throughout this procedure.
    - Put the safety ON, if applicable, if it can be left on during the unloading process.

2. **R**emove all ammunition as follows:

    - Push the magazine-release button (Figure 116) to remove the magazine (the source of all the ammunition except for possibly one chambered cartridge).
    - Pull the slide to the rear by doing the following:
        - o Hold the handgun in the strong hand and point in a safe direction. Extend arm, locking wrist and elbow.
        - o Grip the rear of the slide with the weak hand. Ensure your hand does not cover the ejection port.
        - o Pull the slide quickly and completely to the rear. This will extract and eject any cartridge or casing from the chamber.
        - o Let any cartridge or casing fall on the shooting bench or range floor and leave it there until you have completed all the steps.
    - Lock the slide to the rear, normally by inserting the slide lock into the slide stop notch, where possible (Figure 117).

3. **O**bserve the chamber to confirm that there is no cartridge or empty casing.

4. **V**erify that the feeding path is clear of ammunition casings or foreign objects. Make certain that the magazine has been removed.

5. **E**xamine the bore for lubricant, rust or other obstructions.

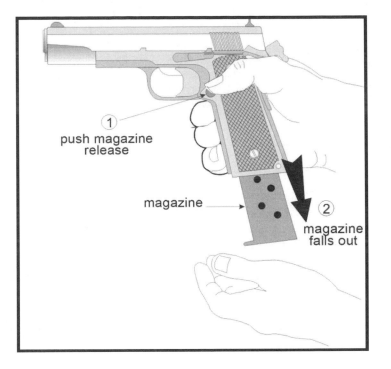

Figure 116. Removing the Magazine from a Semi-automatic

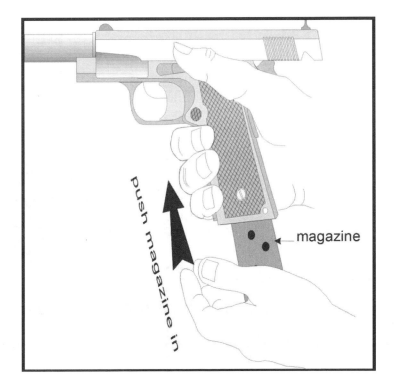

Figure 117. Inserting a Magazine to Load a Semi-automatic

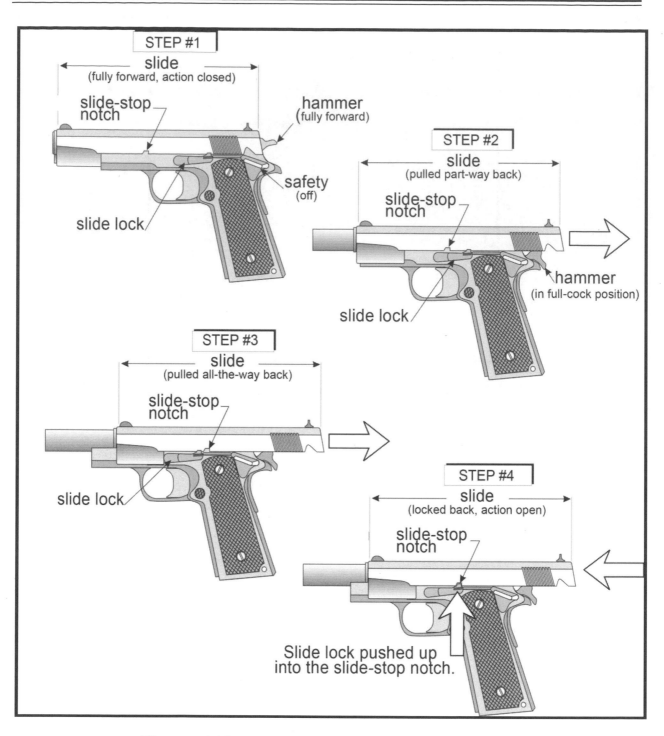

Figure 118. Locking the Slide to the Rear

a. The firearm is now unloaded and safe until it leaves the direct control of the person who unloaded and completed **ACTS** and **PROVEd it safe**.

b. Depending on the make and model of the firearm, magazine releases are located in different places such as the following:

- on the grip behind the trigger; or

- at the bottom of the grip (front or rear).

Consult the owner's manual.

> ⚠ **Direct control is defined as having the firearm within eyesight and/or arm's reach of the shooter.**

14.8.2. Semi-automatic: single action, double action and double action only loading procedure

> ⚠ **Only load a firearm when you intend to use it, and only in an area where it can be safely and legally discharged.**

1. Prepare the firearm for loading by going through the complete unloading procedure—**ACTS and PROVE it safe**.

2. Clear any obstructions from the chamber or barrel. Clean if required.

3. Put the safety **ON**, if applicable, if it can be left on during the loading process.

4. Point the firearm in the safest available direction throughout the loading and chambering process.

5. Make sure that nothing touches the trigger throughout this process.

6. Select the correct ammunition by verifying that the data stamp on the firearm matches the head stamp on the cartridge.

7. Put the firearm down with the muzzle pointed in a safe direction and the action open. Charge the magazine by inserting cartridges into it.

8. Load the firearm by inserting the charged magazine into the magazine well with a firm push until it locks into the firearm.

9. To chamber a cartridge:

- Hold the handgun in the strong hand and point down range. Extend arm, locking wrist and elbow.

- Grip the rear of the slide with the weak hand. Ensure your hand does not cover the ejection port.

- Pull the slide quickly and completely to the rear and allow the slide to slip through your grip at the end of the stroke. The slide will be pushed forward by the recoil spring, chambering a cartridge.

10. Leave the safety on, if applicable, until ready to fire. In the case of certain double-action semi-automatics, activate the decocking lever.

The firearm is now loaded with a charged magazine and a chambered round, ready for use. It requires continuous attention until it is unloaded.

⚠ Always be sure of your target and beyond.

Magazine Capacity Limits

Part 4 of the *Regulations Prescribing Certain Firearms and other Weapons, Components, and Parts of Weapons, Accessories, Cartridge Magazines, Ammunition and Projectiles as Prohibited or Restricted* sets out the limits for the number of cartridges permitted for different types of magazines.

For example, for semi-automatic handguns, the legal magazine capacity maximum is 10 cartridges.
For further information, refer to the Regulations.

Prior to July 1993, owners of large-capacity cartridge magazines that were affected by the limit were able to retain them if they had been properly modified to comply with the law.

14.9. Firearm malfunctions

Generally, when using commercially made ammunition and a properly maintained firearm, malfunctions will not occur. Firearms jammed with a cartridge in the chamber(s) can be hazardous. This hazard, if not dealt with properly, may result in a serious injury. Consult a qualified person or gunsmith for information on how to perform this function in the safest possible manner with your particular firearm.

14.10. Review questions

1. What process is automatic in the semi-automatic handgun?

2. Name the action type of a handgun that only releases the hammer from a cocked position to fire.

3. Name the handgun action that cocks and fires with a single pull of the trigger.

4. Name the safety that requires a magazine in the handgun before it will fire.

5. Name two types of manual safeties used on handguns.

MODULE 15:

FIRING TECHNIQUES AND PROCEDURES FOR HANDGUNS

MODULE 15: FIRING TECHNIQUES AND PROCEDURES FOR HANDGUNS

15.1. Personal safety protection

15.1.0. Overview

Like many active sports, shooting has the potential to cause personal injury. The careful shooter takes steps to avoid these injuries by wearing personal safety protection.

15.1.1. Sight protection

a. There is a risk of eye injury in shooting without eye protection. This can come from ejected cartridge casings. It can also come from fragments and other debris ejected during firing.

b. To avoid these hazards, shooters should wear safety glasses made of impact-resistant glass or polycarbonate plastic with side shields (Figure 119). They also guard against firearm malfunctions or bullet fragments.

Figure 119. Sight and Hearing Protection

15.1.2. Hearing protection

a. Continued unprotected exposure to shooting noise will cause hearing loss. The noise level of a gunshot is similar to that of a jet engine taking off at close range. The need for hearing protection is obvious.

b. Several types of hearing protection are available. On the firing range, shooters should always wear headphone-type hearing protectors. These protectors provide reasonable sound protection. Earplugs are available in several types. Disposable earplugs are made of foam or wax, but they can only be used once.

c. There are also reusable earplugs made of rubber available in several sizes. They require care and cleaning after use.

d. For maximum hearing protection, it is highly recommended that both earplugs and headphone-type hearing protectors be worn.

15.1.3. Slips and falls

a. Slips and falls may occur when handling firearms. This can best be avoided by using common sense.

b. If you do fall, remember your first action should be to control the muzzle of the firearm. This will prevent injury from a discharge. The damage from a fall is probably less than the possible damage from an unintentional discharge.

c. Beware of cumbersome clothing. It can interfere with the safe handling of your firearm.

Occasionally, a hot, ejected cartridge casing may come in contact with unprotected skin. This can cause a shooter to flinch. The sudden movement could result in unsafe muzzle control or discharge. Therefore, button up the collar and sleeves of your shirt or blouse. This way, a hot cartridge casing cannot get inside.

15.2. Introduction to marksmanship

a. Marksmanship is the ability to hit your mark or target. Good marksmanship is important for safe shooting.

b. Marksmanship depends on many factors including grip, shooting position, aim, trigger control, controlled breathing and follow-through. These points are discussed in the following pages.

15.3. Shooting positions

15.3.0. Overview

a. A firm grip gives you complete control of your handgun when it fires. Changing your grip will affect sight alignment and bullet placement on the target.

b. You can fire handguns either one-handed or two-handed and from several positions. Only the basic standing positions are described below.

15.3.1. The two-handed grip

A similar two-handed grip is used for both revolvers and semi-automatics. Point the muzzle down range with your finger off the trigger and out of the trigger guard, until the sights are on the target. Grip the firearm using about the same pressure as you would to hold a carpenter's hammer.

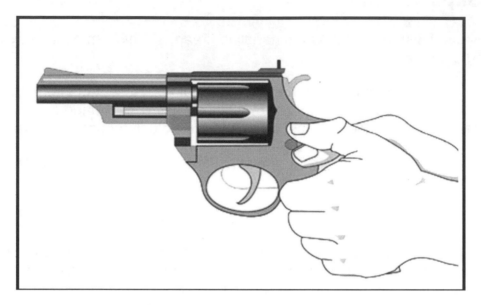

Figure 120. Two-handed Grip for a Revolver

⚠ Using an incorrect two-handed grip, the thumb of the weak hand may be behind the slide. While firing a semi-automatic handgun in this manner, your weak hand can be injured by the recoiling slide. When using the two-handed grip, be certain that your thumbs do not contact the slide and are positioned on the weak-hand side of the handgun.

15.3.2. The two-handed stance

a. Stand with your body facing the target squarely. Spread your feet about shoulder width apart with weight distributed evenly on both feet to give you solid balance. Keep your knees straight but not locked.

b. Stretch out both arms towards the target and lock your elbows. Keep your head up. Control your breathing.

Figure 121. Two-handed Stance

15.3.3. The one-handed grip

⚠️ **Hold the firearm firmly when firing with one hand to avoid losing control.**

Point the muzzle in a safe direction with your finger off the trigger. Wrap your fingers around the grip of the firearm with your thumb resting above the tips of your fingers as shown in the diagram. Hold firmly but not too tightly, using about the same pressure as you would to hold a carpenter's hammer.

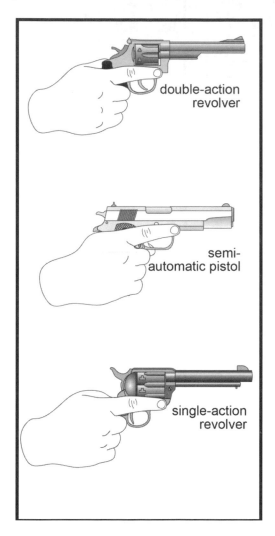

double-action revolver

semi-automatic pistol

single-action revolver

Figure 122. One-handed Grip (right side)

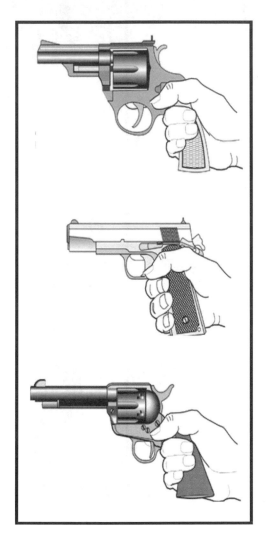

Figure 123. One-handed Grip (left side)

15.3.4. The one-handed stance

a. Stand with your body turned approximately 45 degrees from the target. Spread your feet about shoulder-width apart with weight distributed evenly on both feet to give you solid balance. Keep your knees straight but not locked.

b. Keep the muzzle pointed down range and the barrel parallel to the ground. Stretch out your firing arm towards the target. Lock your elbow and wrist. Keep your head up. Control your breathing.

c. Assume a comfortable position for shooting.

Figure 124. One-handed Stance

15.4. Aiming handguns

A simple technique to use to determine your master eye:

Figure 125. Determining your Master Eye

a. Use your master eye for sighting. It is the stronger of your two eyes and will focus more accurately.

b. To find out which is your master eye, create a triangle using both hands as illustrated in the figure above. With both eyes open, view an object in the distance from the centre of the triangle. With both eyes remaining open, and keeping the object within the triangle, close the left eye and then open the left eye. Then, close the right eye and then open the right eye. The master eye will keep the object in the centre of the triangle. Always try to aim with both eyes open as this gives a better view of the area surrounding the target.

c. You must also learn to correctly use your firearm's sight if your aim is to be accurate. Open sights require you to physically line up both rear and front sights with the target. This process is called sight alignment. When you aim any sight at a target, a sight picture is created (Figure 126).

d. Scope and electronic sights do not require alignment (Figure 127). Scope sights also might have the advantage of magnifying your view of the target.

e. When preparing to aim through a scope or electronic red dot sight, do not look away from the target and then try to find the target again by looking through the scope. Instead, while steadily watching the target, raise the handgun correctly to the two-handed stance with arms fully extended. Point the firearm toward the target area until the sight comes up naturally between your eye and the target.

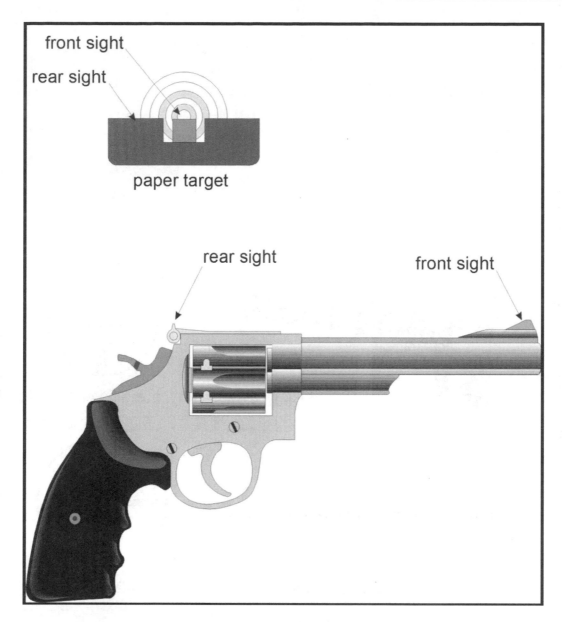

Figure 126. Open Sights Aligned on a Target

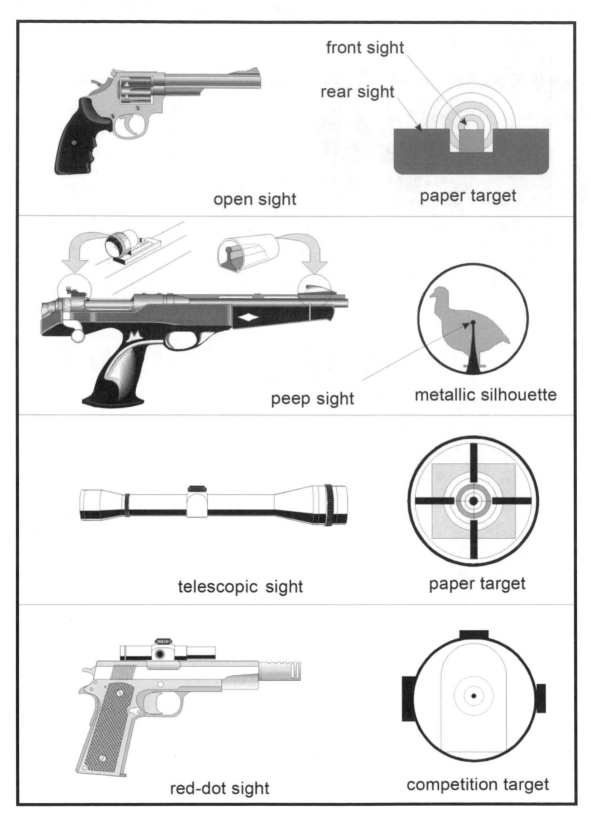

Figure 127. Types of Sights Aligned on Targets

15.5. Review questions

1. When using a revolver with a two-handed grip, is it acceptable to hold your thumbs across each other?

2. When using a semi-automatic handgun with a two-handed grip, why do we hold the thumbs parallel; one over the other and low on the receiver?

3. What is the important consideration to remember regarding your position, when using a one-handed shooting stance?

4. Name two items of personal protective gear you must wear while shooting a handgun.

5. Why should we stand feet shoulder width apart and knees straight but not locked when using the two-handed stance?

MODULE 16:

FUNDAMENTALS OF SHOOTING WITH RESTRICTED FIREARMS

MODULE 16: FUNDAMENTALS OF SHOOTING WITH RESTRICTED FIREARMS

16.1. Sight alignment / Sight picture

You must learn to correctly use your firearm's sights if your aim is to be accurate. Open sights require you to physically line up both rear and front sights with the target. This process is called sight alignment. When you aim any sight at a target a sight picture is created.

16.2. Breathing as it relates to shot release

a. Holding one's breath is not natural. It's not possible to judge how much air is held for each shot release, since there is no gauge on the lungs. The shot must be released in the natural pause of the breathing cycle.

b. We breathe in, we breathe out. There is a natural pause at the bottom of each exhale. It is this natural pause (2.5 seconds) that the shot must be released in. In order to lengthen this natural pause, the shooter has to breathe in deep, force the breath out deeper than normal, breathe in deep again, this time let the breath out normally. The natural pause in the breathing cycle has just been increased to approximately 8.5 seconds. That is plenty of time to confirm sight picture and release the shot, if not, just repeat the process. Breathe in deep, force it out, breathe in deep again, let it out NATURALLY and squeeze the shot off.

c. Figure 128 has been in circulation for over forty years. Unfortunately, some people will sometimes misinterpret it and wrongfully revert to holding their breath.

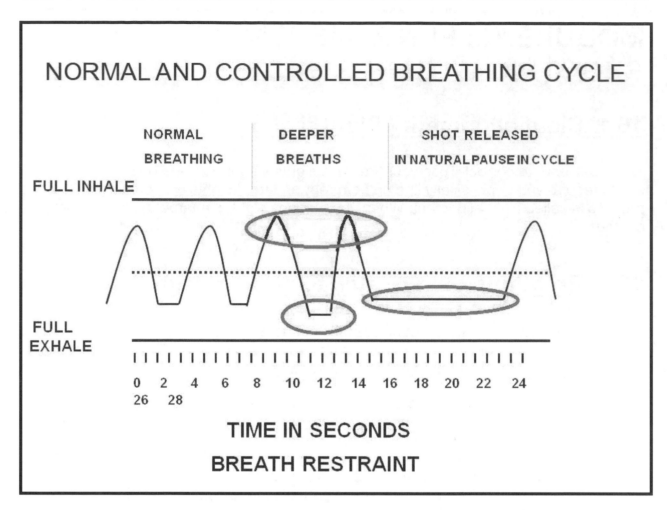

Figure 128. Normal and Controlled Breathing Cycle

16.3. Trigger control

a. Trigger control is essential for accurate shooting. When the sights are aligned on the target, squeeze the trigger slowly and steadily. Avoid yanking or pulling. Anything other than a smooth squeeze will cause the firearm to move and send the shot off target.

b. Don't anticipate the shot.

16.4. Follow-through

This means maintaining your sight picture and/or shooting position after discharging the firearm. If you do not follow-through, it is more likely that your shot will be off target.

16.5. Safety procedures at the range

16.5.1. Range commands

The following are examples of typical range commands:

- "The range is active".

- "Cease-fire".

- "The range is no longer active".

⚠ **Range commands and signals vary between shooting sports, ranges and jurisdictions. Be sure you are aware of and clearly understand the commands and signals used in your area. If you are unsure, ask the Range Officer (RO) or a local official before you go to the range (Appendix G: Visual Range Signals and Devices).**

16.5.2. Range safety rules

⚠ **The Range Officer (RO) is ultimately responsible for the safety of all persons using the range. Commands of the RO must be followed by all shooters at all times.**

Every range has rules on safe behavior. These may vary but will normally include the standard ones shown below:

- Use hearing and sight protection.

- The muzzle must always be pointed down range.

- The action of any firearm must be open at all times except when actually shooting.

- Firearms must be handled, loaded and discharged ONLY at the firing line.

- No firearm is loaded until the command to load is given by the RO.

- Fingers must be kept out of the trigger guard and off the trigger until the firearm is pointed down range.

- Upon the command "cease-fire," all firing stops at once. Firearms are unloaded. Actions are opened. Firearms are laid on the mat or on the table. Their muzzles point in a safe direction down range. The shooter steps back from the firing line, behind the cease-fire line.

- The RO will inspect each firearm before allowing anyone to go forward of the firing line. He will verify that all the actions are open and there is no ammunition in the chambers or chargers.

- During a cease-fire, no one will handle firearms or ammunition or return to the firing line. At this point, wait for further range commands before any further activity. Persons not engaged in changing targets down range should stand well behind the cease-fire line (Figure 129).

⚠ **In an emergency, anyone can call a cease-fire.**

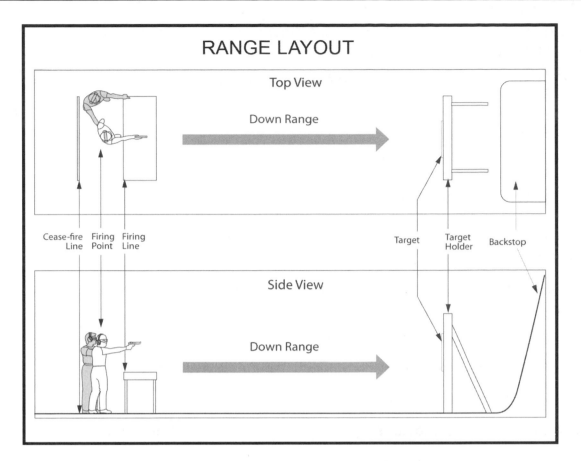

Figure 129. Range Layout with Direct Supervision

Direct control is defined as having the firearm within eyesight and/or arm's reach of the shooter.

There are other rules we recommend you follow:

- Minors and guests who do not have a valid firearms licence must be under direct and immediate supervision while shooting. Consult with your range for any further restrictions.

- Firearms should be checked by the RO on the cease-fire. This is to be sure that all actions are opened and no cartridges are in the breech.

- Unloaded firearms not in use are to be placed on the bench or table with the action open or kept in a case. They must be moved with muzzle pointed in the safest available direction or cased at the firing line.

- Horseplay, careless handling of firearms or any other distraction is not allowed while shooting is in progress.

- Make sure you are using the correct ammunition for your firearm and as approved by the range.

- Never shoot at target holders or other range equipment.

- Do not discharge firearms outside of the approved range property or outside range use times.

16.5.3. Range courtesy

There are certain standards of range courtesy and shooters must follow them. Some of these standards are listed below:

- Rules and procedures vary between ranges. Check and obey local rules. There should be a safety briefing before starting.

- Sign in to the firing range upon arrival.

- Avoid interrupting or distracting others when they are shooting.

- Do not smoke on the firing line.

- Ask the owner's or shooter's permission before handling that person's firearm or equipment.

- Leave enough space between you and others to ensure safety.

- If firing particularly smoky firearms, shoot from downwind of other shooters on the firing line. Black-powder firearms are especially smoky.

- Do not fire on other people's targets, targets not directly down range from yourself, or any target that may disturb others.

- Those firing semi-automatic firearms should take a firing point where other people will not be disturbed by ejected casings.

- Rapid firing may disturb those sighting-in or doing deliberate target work.

 **With the approval of the RO:**

1. **Pick up cartridge casings. Take down targets.**

2. **Put away any range-owned equipment you have used. For example, sandbags or bench rests.**

3. **Sign out when you leave the range.**

16.6. Targets

16.6.1. Acceptable targets

Before firing at any target, verify the target by asking yourself the following questions:

- Is the range active?

- Am I sure I am shooting at my target?

- Are the targets approved by the RO?

16.6.2. Unacceptable targets

Below are examples of unacceptable targets:

- any target which, when fired upon, may damage the range. These include signs and main target holder supports;

- someone else's target on the range;

- any target which is not directly in front of your firing point at the firing line;

- any target which, when fired upon, may disturb others. For example, discharging firearms outside of posted range use times;

- any target or a material or shape that can cause ricochets such as target holder frames or concrete walkways; and

- any target made of glass or other material that causes fragment hazards.

⚠ **The handgun may only be discharged in a place where it is lawful to do so. One such place is a shooting range approved by a CFO. Hunting with a handgun is not permitted.**

16.7. Firearm servicing

⚠ **Ensure that all firearms are unloaded and PROVEd safe before attempting to clean. Refer to Module 14 on unloading procedures—ACTS and PROVE it safe.**

a. Always be sure your firearm is functioning properly. A firearm that does not work properly is an unsafe firearm.

b. This module on minor maintenance and servicing procedures for your firearm is included for general information only. Specific information on cleaning and servicing your firearm is available in your firearm owner's manual, at a gun shop or from a gunsmith. Incidents can occur if these procedures are not performed correctly.

c. Firearms are precision instruments. Even minor repairs should be made by qualified individuals. Unqualified persons should never try to repair or modify any firearm.

d. The average user should do basic cleaning and lubrication only.

16.8. Firearm cleaning

16.8.0. Overview

a. Information on cleaning firearms safely may be obtained from your firearm owner's manual. If you do not have one, contact the manufacturer. Accidents can happen if the cleaning procedure is not performed correctly.

b. Two major threats to firearm safety are as follows:

- rust caused by moisture and condensation; and

- excessive build-up of residue or rust in the firearm.

c. Either may cause excessive pressure, damaging the barrel. This is why regular cleaning is recommended.

d. The barrel of a firearm should be cleaned after every use. This will protect its finish. It will also help keep it in good working order. For instructions on cleaning the rest of the firearm, consult your owner's manual.

e. Modern smokeless primers and powders are non-corrosive. However, some older military surplus ammunition still contains corrosive chemicals. If you use corrosive ammunition, you should clean your firearm immediately after you use it.

f. Any firearm that has been stored for a long time must be cleaned thoroughly before use. Cleaning before using is required when the firearm has been exposed to moisture or dirt.

If cleaning your firearm requires disassembly, consult your owner's manual. If disassembly is required to clean a firearm, always wear safety glasses. Residue or rust in the chamber or barrel may cause serious pressure build-up. Also, oil may mix with unburned powder and other residue may cause the firearm to jam.

16.8.1. Cleaning materials

a. To clean a firearm properly, you need the following materials:

- a cleaning rod and attachments (be sure to use the right size for the firearm), such as a bore brush;

- tips to hold cloth patches;

- patches;

- solvent (also called "bore cleaner");

- gun oil; and

- a soft cloth.

b. If possible, clean your firearm from the breech toward the muzzle. Avoid cleaning from the muzzle toward the breech.

c. However, you may have to clean some types from the muzzle end. In this case, lock the breech open. This permits the passage of the cleaning rod completely through the barrel. You will find a pull-through cleaning device helpful. Avoid rubbing the cleaning rod on the muzzle. Damage to the crown at the muzzle may occur. It is beneficial to insert a cloth into the open action to collect residue, to prevent dirt from entering the action, and to prevent damage to the firearm.

d. When cleaning a bolt action, remove the bolt, if possible. Clean the firearm from the breech end. Some firearms are easier to clean if you remove the barrel first.

! **While cleaning a firearm, remember and follow the Vital Four ACTS. These additional recommended practices for home safety with firearms might prevent accidents:**

- **Make sure no ammunition is nearby during cleaning.**

- **Never allow a loaded firearm in any building or living area.**

- **Always give cleaning your firearm your full attention. Never clean a firearm while doing something else, like watching television.**

16.8.2. General cleaning procedures

1. Attach the bore brush to the cleaning rod. Apply bore cleaner to the brush.

2. Run the brush through the bore of the barrel/chamber(s) several times. Be sure that the brush sticks out completely. Then draw it back through the barrel (Figure 130).

   NOTE: When cleaning a revolver, always support the cylinder to avoid potential damage.

3. Remove the bore brush from the cleaning rod. Attach a patch-holder tip and a proper size cloth patch. Pour solvent on the cloth patch. Run through the bore of the barrel/chamber(s) several times. Remove the cloth patch from the rod tip.

4. Next, run a clean, dry patch through the bore/chamber(s) several times.

5. If the patch comes out dirty, repeat the first four steps. Do this until a patch finally comes through clean.

6. Next, run a lightly oiled patch through the bore/chamber(s). Use only light gun oil.

7. Wipe the outside of the firearm with a clean cloth and apply a light coat of gun oil or rust preventative to the metal surfaces. You should also maintain the condition of the stock by applying the appropriate wood treatment (consult the owner's manual).

8. Always store your firearm lawfully in accordance with regulations.

9. Remember, before the next firing of the firearm, run a dry patch through the bore and the chamber(s) to remove any oil.

10. Don't forget to clean your magazine.

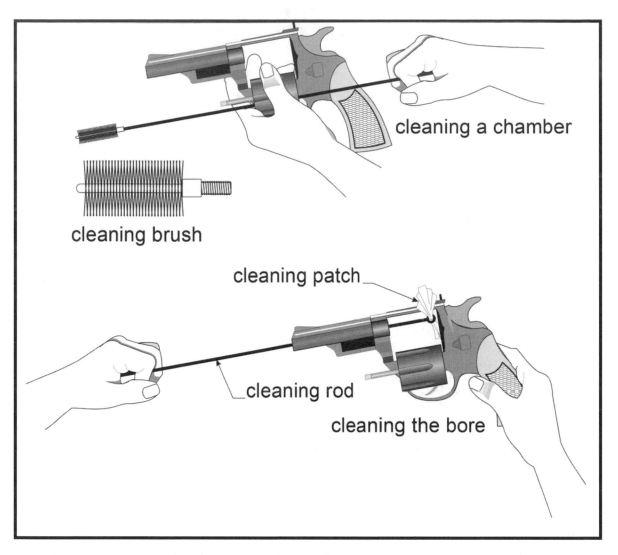

cleaning a chamber

cleaning brush

cleaning patch

cleaning rod

cleaning the bore

Figure 130. Cleaning a Double-action Revolver Cylinder

⚠ **After cleaning a firearm for storage, avoid skin contact with metal parts. Acids in perspiration can cause rust.**

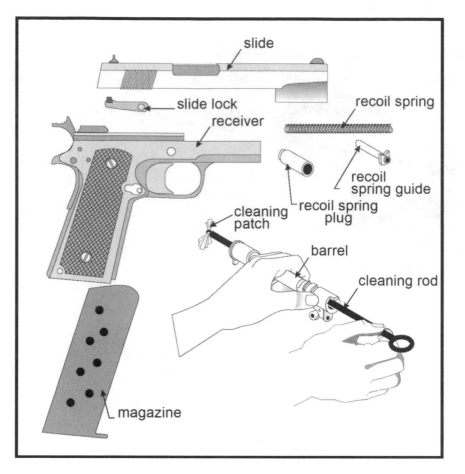

Figure 131. Cleaning a Semi-automatic Handgun

16.8.3. Cleaning ammunition

a. Ammunition should also be kept clean and dry. Oil, sand or dirt on the cartridge can damage the firearm. If could also cause jamming of the action.

b. Avoid exposing your ammunition to heat and vibration. Powder can decay and become unpredictable if exposed to excessive heat and long-term vibration.

⚠ Primers are adversely affected by exposure to penetrating oils. Do not clean your ammunition with an oily rag. Before using any firearm, remove oil or grease from inside the barrel. Increased pressure caused by dirt or oil may cause the barrel to burst. This comes from the pressure generated in a dirty barrel when a bullet is fired through it. After storage and before you use the firearm again, run a clean patch through the bore. Remove all grease and oil. Always ensure your firearm is in good working order. Ensure that you have followed the Vital Four ACTS in order to PROVE the firearm safe before attempting to clean and throughout the entire cleaning procedure.

16.9. Review questions

1. Name the process of maintaining your sight picture after firing.

2. Should you step to the firing line and reload your handgun after a "cease-fire" is called?

3. Having the firearm within eyesight and/or arm's reach of the shooter is described as…

4. Is a shooter permitted to shoot cross range at a target not in use by another shooter?

5. Describe the supervision of minors at the range.

MODULE 17:

SAFE STORAGE, DISPLAY, TRANSPORTATION AND HANDLING OF RESTRICTED FIREARMS

MODULE 17: SAFE STORAGE, DISPLAY, TRANSPORTATION AND HANDLING OF RESTRICTED FIREARMS

17.1. Classes of firearms

17.1.0. Overview

Below you will find brief descriptions of each class of firearms. For legal references, however, please refer to the *Firearms Act* and its Regulations, and Part III of the *Criminal Code*.

⚠️ **It must be noted that some rifles and shotguns are considered restricted or prohibited. Persons wishing to acquire such firearms should contact the Provincial or Territorial authorities or call the CFP at 1-800-731-4000.**

Restricted Firearms
In general, individuals may possess restricted firearms for one or more of the following reasons: lawful profession or occupation, target practice or competition or as part of a gun collection. The following are examples of restricted firearms: • A handgun that is not a prohibited firearm; • A firearm that is not a prohibited firearm, has a barrel less than 470 mm (18½ inches) in length, and discharges centre-fire ammunition in a semi-automatic manner; • A firearm that is designed or adapted to be fired when reduced to a length of less than 660 mm (26 inches) by folding, telescoping or otherwise; and • A firearm of any kind that is prescribed by regulation to be a restricted firearm.

Prohibited Firearms

In general, individuals cannot acquire the types of firearms that fall into the prohibited class. Depending on the nature of their duties, employees of business and carriers, and public officers (police or peace officer, firearms officer, prescribed employee of a federal, provincial or municipal government) may possess prohibited firearms. The following are examples of prohibited firearms:

- Handguns with a barrel length equal to or less than 105 mm (4⅛ inches);

- Handguns designed or adapted to discharge a 25 or 32 calibre cartridge (any of the above-noted handguns are not prohibited firearms if they are used in competitions governed by the rules of the *International Shooting Sport Federation* and prescribed by regulation);

- "Sawed-off" rifles or "sawed-off" shotguns less than 660 mm (26 inches) in length;

- "Sawed-off" rifles or "sawed-off" shotguns 660 mm (26 inches) or greater in length and have barrel lengths of less than 457 mm (18 inches);

- An automatic firearm; and

- Any firearm that is prescribed by regulation to be a prohibited firearm.

17.2. Ammunition, prohibited ammunition and prohibited devices

17.2.0. Overview

Ammunition, prohibited ammunition and prohibited devices are defined in the Part III of the *Criminal Code*. The table below provides a brief description of prohibited devices. For a complete description of all of the aforementioned, consult the *Criminal Code* of Canada.

17.2.1. Prohibited devices

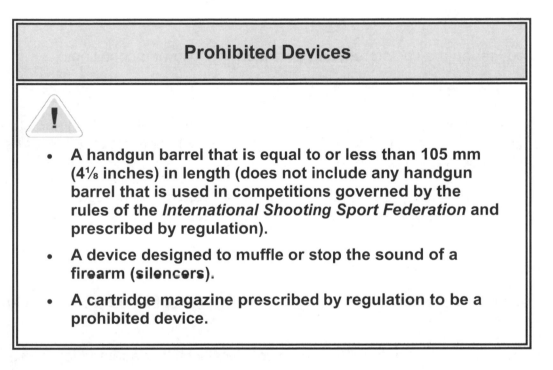

Prohibited Devices
<ul><li>**A handgun barrel that is equal to or less than 105 mm (4⅛ inches) in length (does not include any handgun barrel that is used in competitions governed by the rules of the *International Shooting Sport Federation* and prescribed by regulation).**</li><li>**A device designed to muffle or stop the sound of a firearm (silencers).**</li><li>**A cartridge magazine prescribed by regulation to be a prohibited device.**</li></ul>

Refer to the appropriate sections of *the Firearms Acts* and Regulations for detailed requirements relating to the storage, display, transportation and handling of restricted firearms.

a. **Remember, you are responsible for your firearms 24 hours a day.** Anyone who owns or uses a firearm must meet safe storage, display, transportation and handling requirements. These requirements are set out in the *Storage, Display, Transportation and Handling of Firearms by Individuals Regulations*. All of these are described in this module.

b. Firearm owners and users should always assume that anyone untrained in the safe handling and use of firearms does not know how to handle firearms safely. Incidents could occur from unauthorized access, especially where children are concerned. To prevent a tragedy, always store, display, transport and handle firearms and ammunition in accordance with the Regulations.

c. Remember the law requires that all restricted firearms can only be loaded and discharged in an approved or legal area.

17.3. Storage

A restricted firearm may be stored, only if it meets the following conditions:

- It is unloaded, and

  o rendered inoperable by using a secure locking device (Figure 132) and stored in a securely locked container (Figure 133), receptacle or room that cannot be easily broken open or into, or

  o stored in a securely locked vault (Figure 134), safe or room (Figure 135) specifically built or adapted for the secure storage of restricted firearms; and

- Not within easy access to ammunition, unless the ammunition is stored, together with or separately from the firearm in:

  o a securely locked container or receptacle that cannot be easily broken open or into, or

  o a securely locked vault, safe or room specifically built or adapted for the secure storage of restricted firearms.

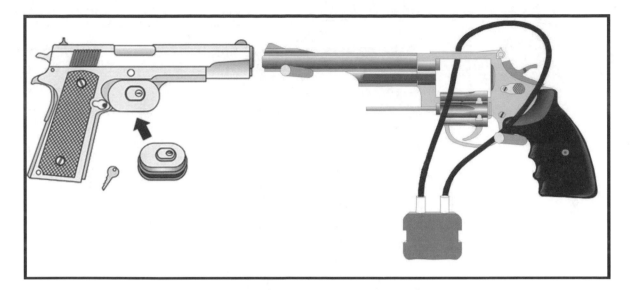

Figure 132. Cable and Trigger Locks

⚠ A restricted firearm may only be stored at the address located on the registration. Keep in mind that storing ammunition in an unvented container may create an explosive hazard during a fire.

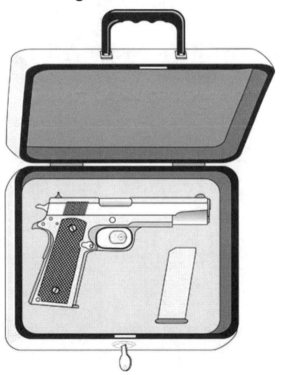

Figure 133. Lockable Carrying/Storage Case

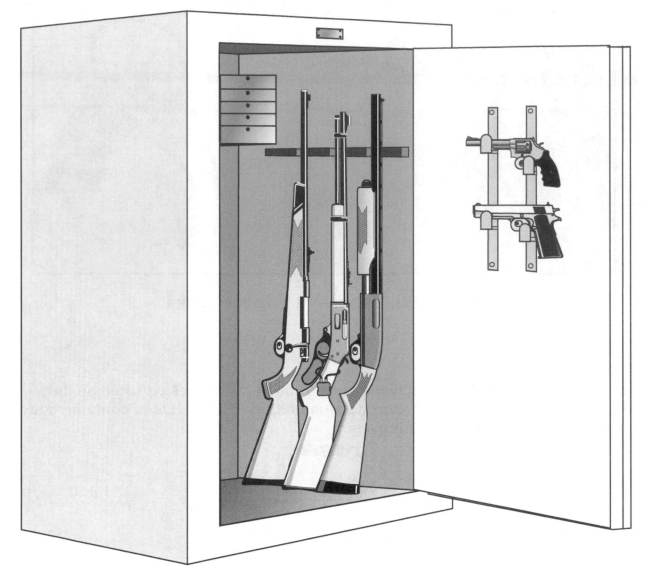

Figure 134. Storage Vault (safe)

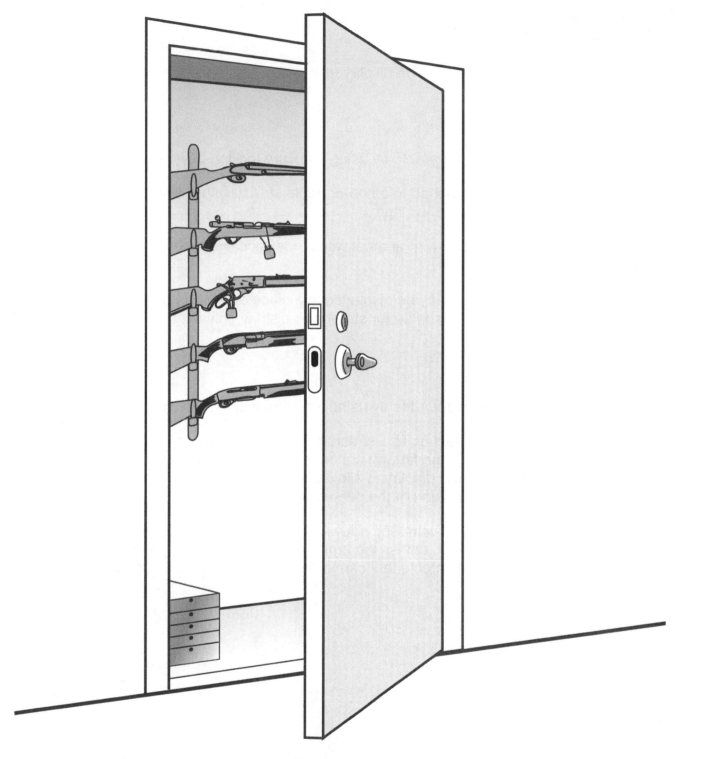

Figure 135. Secure Room (restricted firearms)

17.4. Display

a. A restricted firearm may be displayed in a dwelling house only under the following conditions:

- it is unloaded;

- it is rendered inoperable by using a secure locking device;

- it is securely attached to a non-portable structure that cannot be easily removed (Figure 136); and

- it is not displayed with and not within easy access to ammunition that can be discharged from it.

b. A restricted firearm may be displayed in a place other than at the legal address where the firearm has to be for storage or display only if it meets the following conditions:

- it is unloaded;

- it is rendered inoperable by using a secure locking device;

- it is securely attached to a structure by a chain, metal cable or similar device in a manner that the firearm cannot be easily removed; (a firearm may be removed from the display to allow someone to handle it, if the firearm is under the direct supervision of the person displaying it); and

- it is not displayed with, and not within easy access to, ammunition that can be discharged from it, unless the ammunition is displayed in a securely locked container or receptacle that cannot be easily broken open or into.

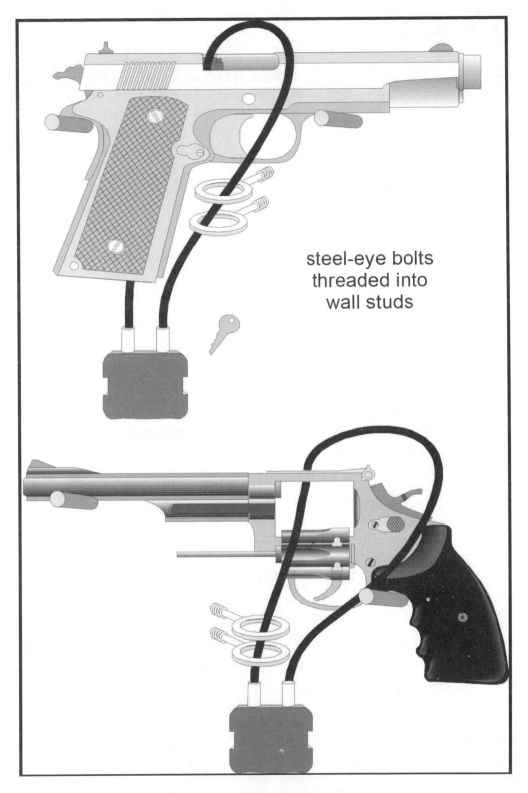

steel-eye bolts
threaded into
wall studs

Figure 136. Display

17.5. Transportation

a. When transporting your restricted firearm between two or more specific places, you will need an "Authorization to Transport." To obtain an "Authorization to Transport," you need to contact a CFO or call 1-800-731-4000. You will need to provide the following information: your firearms licence number, the registration certificate number of the firearm(s) to be transported, the frequency, dates and times the firearm(s) will be transported, the place of departure and destination of the transported firearms, and the reason for transporting the firearm(s).

 Please note: provincial/territorial policies may also apply.

b. A restricted firearm may be transported only under the following conditions:

- It is unloaded, and

  - rendered inoperable by using a secure locking device; and

  - in a locked container that is made of an opaque material and cannot be easily broken open or into or accidentally opened during transportation. A heavy-duty soft case (i.e., made of nylon) meets these requirements as long as you can lock it securely.

- You may leave the locked container (carrying the restricted firearm) in an unattended vehicle's securely locked trunk or similar compartment.

- If the unattended vehicle does not have a securely locked trunk or similar compartment, lock the vehicle, or the part of the vehicle that contains the container, and leave the locked container out of sight.

IMPORTANT: Removing the firing pin or any other component of a restricted or prohibited handgun <u>does not</u> meet the requirement for safe transport.

If you want to transport firearms on an aircraft, you should first contact the air carrier. The air carrier will provide information on its regulations and requirements.

17.6. Handling

a. Before obtaining a restricted firearm, think about how you will transport it home. The law requires that all restricted firearms be transported unloaded and rendered inoperable with a secure locking device. They must also be in a locked opaque case or container (Figure 137).

b. There are locations where discharging a firearm violates federal or provincial acts and regulations, or municipal bylaws. It may also be an offence to load or handle firearms in these places. You may load a firearm or handle a loaded firearm only in a place where it is lawful to discharge it.

⚠ **A restricted firearm may only be loaded and discharged in a place where it can be safely and legally discharged.**

Figure 137. Lockable Carrying/Storage Case

Every person commits an offence who, without lawful excuse, points a firearm at another person, whether the firearm is loaded or unloaded, and is

1. **guilty of an indictable offence and liable imprisonment for a term not exceeding five years; or**

2. **guilty of an offence punishable on summary conviction (a fine of $5,000 and/or six months imprisonment).**

Reference: Subsections 87(1) and (2) of Part III of the *Criminal Code*

Every person who stores, displays, transports or handles any firearm in a manner contrary to the *Storage, Display, Transportation and Handling of Firearms by Individuals Regulations* is

1. **guilty of an indictable offence and liable to imprisonment,**

   - **in the case of a first offence, for a term not exceeding two years, and**

   - **in the case of a second or subsequent offence, for a term not exceeding five years; or**

2. **guilty of an offence punishable on summary conviction (a fine of $5,000 and/or six months imprisonment).**

Reference: Subsections 86(2) and (3) of Part III of the *Criminal Code*

They may also lose their firearm, lose their licence, receive a fine, receive jail time and/or be prohibited from possessing a firearm for a period of time.

The Vital Four ACTS of Firearm Safety

👉	**Assume every firearm is loaded.** • Regard any firearm as a potential danger.
👉	**Control the muzzle direction at all times.** • Identify the safest available muzzle direction. • Keep the firearm pointed in the safest available direction. • The muzzle of a firearm should not be pointed towards yourself or any other person.
👉	**Trigger finger must be kept off the trigger and out of the trigger guard.** • Do **NOT** put your finger on the trigger or inside the trigger guard when you pick up a firearm.
👉	**See that the firearm is unloaded—PROVE it safe.** • Do not handle the firearm unless you can properly **PROVE** it safe. • Check to see that both chamber and magazine are empty. Do this every time you handle a firearm, for any reason. • Pass or accept only open and unloaded firearms. It is an essential rule to adopt.

PROVE it safe	
👉	**P**oint the firearm in the safest available direction.
👉	**R**emove all ammunition.
👉	**O**bserve the chamber.
👉	**V**erify the feeding path.
👉	**E**xamine the bore for obstructions.

The firearm is now unloaded and safe until it leaves the direct control of the person who unloaded and PROVEd it safe.

⚠ **Direct control is defined as having the firearm within eyesight and/or arm's reach of the shooter. Only load a firearm when you intend to use it, and only in an area where it can be safely and legally discharged.**

17.7. Review questions

1. List three reasons permitting you to possess a handgun.

2. Describe the legal parameters of handgun storage.

3. List the documents you must carry when transporting your handgun to the range.

4. Is it legal to store your restricted firearm at your friend's house?

5. List the legal requirements for transporting a restricted handgun.

APPENDICES

APPENDICES

Overview

These appendices are provided for general information purposes only. The information contained in this section may be additional to that contained in the course. Information contained in the Appendix will not form part of the written or practical tests.

For legal references, please refer to the actual legislation, namely the *Firearms Act* and its Regulations, and Part III of the *Criminal Code*.

Appendix A: Antique firearms

An antique firearm refers to any firearm manufactured before 1898 that was not designed or redesigned to discharge rim-fire or centre-fire ammunition, plus any other firearm specifically identified as an antique by the Regulations. Owners of antique firearms do not need to have a firearms licence or a registration certificate. There are also no restrictions on the transfer of antique firearms. However, antique firearm owners must comply with the requirements found in the *Storage, Display, Transportation and Handling of Firearms by Individuals Regulations.*

Source: Section 84, Part III of the *Criminal Code*, Paragraph 117(*h*), *Firearms Act*

Appendix B: Buying ammunition

Any individual wishing to buy ammunition in Canada must have a valid Canadian firearms licence. (Non-residents must have either a confirmed declaration or a temporary borrowing licence to buy ammunition in Canada.)

Appendix C: Legal definitions

The following definitions are taken from the *Firearms Act* and its Regulations, and Part III of the *Criminal Code*.

ammunition: A cartridge containing a projectile designed to be discharged from a firearm and, without restricting the generality of the foregoing, includes a caseless cartridge and a shot shell. *(munitions)*

antique firearm: (1) Any firearm manufactured before 1898 that was not designed to discharge rim-fire or centre-fire ammunition and that has not been redesigned to discharge such ammunition. (2) Any firearm that is prescribed to be an antique firearm. *(arme à feu historique)*

firearm: A barrelled weapon from which any shot, bullet or other projectile can be discharged and that is capable of causing serious bodily injury or death to a person, and includes any frame or receiver of such a barrelled weapon and anything that can be adapted for use as a firearm. *(arme à feu)*

handgun: A firearm that is designed, altered or intended to be aimed and fired by the action of one hand, whether or not it has been redesigned or subsequently altered to be aimed and fired by the action of both hands. *(arme de poing)*

non-restricted firearm: A firearm that is neither a prohibited firearm nor a restricted firearm. *(arme à feu sans restrictions)*

prohibited ammunition: Ammunition, or a projectile of any kind, that is prescribed to be prohibited ammunition. *(munitions prohibées)*

prohibited device: (1) Any component or part of a weapon, or any accessory for use with a weapon, that is prescribed to be a prohibited device. (2) A handgun barrel that is equal to or less than 105 mm in length, but does not include any such handgun barrel that is prescribed, where the handgun barrel is for use in international sporting competitions governed by the rules of the International Shooting Sport Federation. (3) A device or contrivance designed or intended to muffle or stop the sound or report of a firearm. (4) A cartridge magazine that is prescribed to be a prohibited device. (5) A replica firearm. *(dispositif prohibé)*

prohibited firearm: (1) A handgun that has a barrel equal to or less than 105 mm in length, or is designed or adapted to discharge a 25- or 32-calibre cartridge, but does not include any such handgun that is prescribed, where the handgun is for use in international sporting competitions governed by the rules of the International Shooting Sport Federation. (2) A firearm that is adapted from a rifle or shotgun, whether by sawing, cutting or any other alteration, and that, as so adapted, is less than 660 mm in length, or is 660 mm or greater in length and has a barrel less than 457 mm in length. (3) An automatic firearm, whether or not it has been altered to discharge only one projectile with one pressure of the trigger. (5) Any firearm that is prescribed to be a prohibited firearm. *(arme à feu prohibée)*

replica firearm: Any device that is designed or intended to exactly resemble, or to resemble with near precision, a firearm, and that itself is not a firearm, but does not include any such device that is designed or intended to exactly resemble, or to resemble with near precision, an antique firearm. *(réplique)*

restricted firearm: (1) A handgun that is not a prohibited firearm. (2) A firearm that is not a prohibited firearm, has a barrel less than 470 mm in length, and is capable of discharging centre-fire ammunition in a semi-automatic manner. (3) A firearm that is designed or adapted to be fired when reduced to a length of less than 660 mm by folding, telescoping or otherwise. (4) A firearm of any other kind that is prescribed to be a restricted firearm. *(arme à feu à autorisation restreinte)*

secure locking device: A device that can only be opened or released by the use of an electronic, magnetic or mechanical key or by setting the device in accordance with an alphabetical or numerical combination; and that, when applied to a firearm, prevents the firearm from being discharged. *(dispositif de verrouillage sécuritaire)*

unattended: In respect of a vehicle, means that the vehicle is not under the direct and immediate supervision of a person who is 18 years of age or older or to whom a licence has been issued under the Act. *(non surveillé)*

unloaded: In respect of a firearm, means that any propellant, projectile or cartridge that can be discharged from the firearm is not contained in the breech or firing chamber of the firearm nor in the cartridge magazine attached to or inserted into the firearm. *(non chargée)*

vehicle: Any conveyance that is used for transportation by water, land or air. *(véhicule)*

<u>Appendix D: Personal firearms inventory (example)</u>

MAKE:

MODEL:

SERIAL NO:

FIREARM IDENTIFICATION NUMBER:

MANUFACTURER:

BARREL LENGTH:

CALIBRE / GAUGE:

REGISTRATION CERTIFICATE NUMBER:

PURCHASED FROM:

DATE OF PURCHASE:

VALUE:

DISTINGUISHING MARKS:

ACCESSORIES (case, grips, etc.):

Appendix E: Replica firearms

A replica firearm is designed or intended to exactly, or almost exactly, resemble a firearm, but itself is not a firearm. Under Part III of the *Criminal Code*, a replica firearm is a prohibited device. Owners of replica firearms do not need to have a firearms licence or a registration certificate. However, replica firearm owners must comply with the transportation requirements found in the *Storage, Display, Transportation and Handling of Firearms by Individuals Regulations.*

Source: Section 84, Part III of the *Criminal Code*, Paragraph 117(*i*), *Firearms Act*

Appendix F: Reporting lost or stolen firearms, licences, etc.

Where a firearm or other weapon is lost or stolen, or a licence, registration certificate or authorization is lost or stolen—it must be reported.

A person commits an offence if after having lost a firearm, a prohibited weapon, a restricted weapon, a prohibited device, any prohibited ammunition, an authorization, a licence or a registration certificate, or having had it stolen, does not report the loss or theft with reasonable dispatch to a peace officer, firearms officer, or Chief Firearms Officer (CFO).

Similarly, a person commits an offence, if on finding a firearm, a prohibited weapon, a restricted weapon, a prohibited device, or any prohibited ammunition, does not report the find, or deliver the item with reasonable dispatch to a peace officer, firearms officer, or CFO. This offence does not extend to documents, specifically an authorization, a licence or a registration certificate.

Commission of either offence is punishable on summary conviction or by indictment.

Source: Section 105, Part III of the *Criminal Code*

Appendix G: Visual range signals and devices

Flags or Signs: Typically a red flag flown at or near the entrance to the property. It serves to warn people that live fire may occur at any time and that shooters are actively using one or more ranges. Some clubs have individual "in use" flags for each range.

Down Range Activity Signals: Typically a red light, rope, or red flag at the entrance to the down range area. Red means stop! Do not go down range. A few clubs use a green flag or light to indicate it is safe to go down range. This display should NOT be visible from the shooting positions! Some ranges fly "down range" red flags to show it is NOT safe to discharge firearms; this is potentially confusing unless the flag cannot be seen by people in the down range area.

Shooting Line Activity Signals: Typically a red light, a red flashing light, a red flag, or a baffle clearly visible to the shooter when in the shooting position. Red means stop shooting! On some indoor ranges, the white lights that illuminate the firing line are dimmed and red illumination supplied. This display should NOT be positioned or used in a manner to be confused with the red signal at the entry to the down range area. Some ranges fly "down range" green flags to show that the range is safe for live fire; this is potentially confusing unless the flag cannot be seen by people in the down range area.

Appendix H: Gun collector

The *Firearms Act* recognizes that collecting firearms is a legitimate reason for owning firearms. The rules on gun collecting apply to restricted firearms and to "grandfathered" prohibited handguns with barrel lengths of 105 mm or less, or 25 and 32 calibre. In order to collect grandfathered handguns, an individual must have registered one such handgun as of December 1, 1998, and then continuously thereafter maintained a registration for one such handgun. In order to qualify as a gun collector, a person must:

- have knowledge of the historical, technical or scientific characteristics of the firearms that are part of a collection;

- give signed consent to periodic inspections of the area where the collection is stored; and

- comply with safe storage, display, handling and transportation standards.

When a person acquires a restricted firearm or prohibited handgun, or when he or she renews their firearms licence, the Chief Firearms Officer must determine whether the firearm is being acquired, or firearms already in possession are for the purpose of gun collection.

Source: Sections 67, 28 and 30, *Firearms Act*

Appendix I: Firearms licences

Under the *Firearms Act*, anyone wishing to possess, borrow, buy, inherit or otherwise acquire firearms must have a valid firearms licence.

The *Firearms Act* and *Firearms Licences Regulations* set out the following types of individual firearms licences:

- Possession and Acquisition Licence (PAL);
- Minor's Possession licence;
- Non-resident Sixty-day Possession Licence (Borrowed Firearms); and
- Non-resident Firearm Declaration (Confirmation of Importation of a Firearm by a Non-resident).

Requirements for obtaining firearms licences are the same across Canada.

Possession and Acquisition Licence

This type of licence is required for anyone wishing to acquire firearms, whether for the first time or in addition to the firearms already owned. An individual must successfully complete the Canadian Firearms Safety Course and tests to obtain the licence for non-restricted firearms. To obtain the licence for restricted firearms and/or prohibited firearms an individual must also successfully complete the Canadian Restricted Firearms Safety Course and tests. There is a minimum 28-day waiting period for this licence, unless the applicant already holds a valid PAL or Minor's Possession licence.

Appendix J: Transferring restricted firearms

Sections 22 and 23 of the *Firearms Act* set out a number of conditions that must be satisfied by both parties involved in the transfer of a restricted firearm before the transfer is authorized. In addition, there are a number of conditions that apply in the *Conditions of Transferring Firearms and Other Weapons Regulations*.

The following outlines the information that must be provided when individuals transfer (sell, barter, or give away) firearms.

Transferor's Obligations

An individual who wants to transfer a firearm must:

- be reasonably sure that the transferee does not have a mental illness which would give rise to public safety concerns;

- be reasonably sure that the transferee is not impaired by alcohol or drugs;

- require the transferee to show a valid licence which authorizes the transferee to acquire and possess the particular class of firearm;

- be satisfied that the licence shown authorizes the transferee to acquire and possess the particular class of firearm;

- inform a Chief Firearms Officer (CFO) of the transfer and obtain his or her authorization; and

- ensure that the following conditions (subsection 2(1) of the *Conditions of Transferring Firearms and Other Weapons Regulations*) are complied with:

  o provide the CFO with the transferor's and transferee's name and address;

  o provide the CFO with the transferor's and transferee's licence numbers; and

  o provide the registration certificate number of the firearm being transferred to the CFO.

Transferee's Obligations

In order for a transfer to be authorized, the individual to whom the firearms will be transferred must:

- hold a valid Possession and Acquisition Licence for the particular class of firearm;

- ensure that a new registration certificate is issued by the Registrar;

- for the transfer of restricted firearms and prohibited handguns (pre-December 1, 1998) only,

  o inform the CFO why he or she needs to acquire the firearms (lawful profession or occupation, target practice or competition, or part of a gun collection); and

  o if the transferee is acquiring the firearm to form part of a gun collection, he or she will have to provide the CFO with:

    ▪ information regarding his or her knowledge of characteristics which relate or distinguish the restricted firearms or handguns that he or she possesses;

    ▪ signed consent to reasonably conducted periodic inspections of the area where the collection is kept; and

    ▪ details of his or her knowledge of safe storage requirements for restricted firearms or prohibited handguns;

- for the transfer of restricted and prohibited firearms only, provide the CFO with the number of the registration certificate issued to him or her.

Before authorizing a transfer, the CFO must determine whether or not the transfer will affect the safety of others. If the transfer is authorized, the CFO will issue a unique transfer authorization number to both parties. Where transfers are completed by telephone, the transfer number provided to both parties will serve as a confirmation of the transfer and as a temporary registration certificate until a new registration certificate is sent in the mail.

Annex K: Transferring a non-restricted firearm

On April 5, 2012, Bill C-19, ending the *Long-Gun Registry Act*, came into effect ending the requirement for a transferor of a non-restricted firearm to wait for confirmation of the Transfer approval prior to releasing the non-restricted firearm to the transferee. The transferor must be satisfied that the transferee is a holder of a valid Possession and Acquisition Licence, with the proper privileges of acquisition, before transfer is finalized.

Sections 22 and 23 of the *Firearms Act* set out a number of conditions that must be satisfied by both parties involved in the transfer of a non-restricted firearm before the transfer is authorized. In addition, there are a number of conditions that apply in the *Conditions of Transferring Firearms and Other Weapons Regulations*.

The following outlines the information that must be provided when individuals transfer (sell, barter, or give away) firearms.

Transferor's Obligations

An individual who wants to transfer a firearm must:

- be reasonably sure that the transferee does not have a mental illness which would give rise to public safety concerns;

- be reasonably sure that the transferee is not impaired by alcohol or drugs; and

- require the transferee to show a valid licence which authorizes the transferee to acquire and possess the particular class of firearm;

Transferee's Obligations

In order for a transfer to be authorized, the individual to whom the firearms will be transferred must:

- hold a valid Possession and Acquisition Licence for the particular class of firearm.

GLOSSARY

GLOSSARY

A

action: The moving parts of a firearm that load, fire, extract and eject ammunition.

action release: The part of a firearm that unlatches or opens the action to give access to the chamber.

air gun: A firearm that uses compressed air or carbon dioxide to propel a projectile.

ammunition: See under Appendix C: Legal Definitions.

antique firearm: See under Appendix C: Legal Definitions.

aperture sight: A rear sight with a hole for viewing the target. Also known as a peep sight.

automatic: An action that fires cartridges in rapid succession during one sustained pressure of the trigger.

B

ball:
a) A lead projectile fired by black-powder firearms.
b) Full-metal jacket ammunition.

ballistics: The study of projectiles in flight and what affects them. This means the barrel, in flight and within the target, including trajectory, force, impact and penetration.

barrel: The metal tube of a firearm. The bullet, shot or projectile accelerates down it when the firearm is fired.

barrel length: The distance from the muzzle to the chamber, including the chamber itself. This measurement does not include accessories or barrel extensions like flash suppressors or muzzle brakes. The barrel length of a revolver is the distance from the muzzle to the breech end immediately in front of the cylinder.

BB gun: A type of air gun designed to use spherical steel BB pellets.

big bore: A rifle shooting term that refers to centre-fire firearms or ammunition.

black powder: A finely ground powder, mainly used in muzzleloaders and antique cartridge firearms. The basic ingredients are saltpetre (potassium nitrate), charcoal (carbon) and sulphur.

blueing or bluing: An oxidation (rust) process applied to firearm metal parts. Controlled by applying oil that mixes with the nitrates used in the process. The oil prevents further rusting by sealing the metal. This gives the metal a blue/black colour that resulted in the name "bluing."

boat tail: The tapered rear end of some bullets, used to increase ballistic efficiency at long range.

bolt: A steel rod-like assembly that moves back and forth in an action, sealing the cartridge in the chamber during firing.

bolt action: A repeating firearm that has a magazine and in which the breech bolt or closure device operates in line with the bore; manually operated by a permanent projection or handle attached to the bolt or closure device.

bolt face: The forward end of the bolt that supports the base of the cartridge.

bore: The inside of the barrel of a firearm excluding the chamber. The channel through which the bullet or other projectile is fired from the gun.

bore diameter: The measurement from one side of the bore to the other. See also **rifling**; **calibre**.

breech: The rear end of the barrel into which the ammunition is loaded. See also **chamber**.

breechblock: The part in the breech mechanism that locks the action against the firing of the cartridge.

breechloader: A firearm loaded through the breech.

buckshot: Large lead pellets used in shotgun shells.

bullet: A projectile designed to be fired from a rifled barrel.

butt: The rear end of a rifle or shotgun (the portion that rests against the shoulder). In a handgun, the bottom part of the grip.

buttstock: In long guns, the part of the stock which extends from the receiver to the butt.

C

calibre: A measurement in metric or imperial units to describe the inside diameter of the barrel of a rifled firearm. Calibre is also used to describe the diameter of a projectile in a cartridge.

cap: See **percussion cap**.

carbine: A light short-barrelled rifle.

cartridge: A complete unit of ammunition consisting of a case, primer, powder and a projectile. Modern cartridges are generally classified into two categories: centre-fire and rim-fire. See also **shell**.

cartridge magazine: A device or container from which ammunition may be fed into the firing chamber of a firearm. Part 4 of the *Regulations Prescribing Certain Firearms and other Weapons, Components, and Parts of Weapons, Accessories, Cartridge Magazines, Ammunition and Projectiles as Prohibited or Restricted* sets out the limit for the number of cartridges permitted for different types of magazines. The two common types are box-type magazine and tubular magazine.

case: Also called casing. The container of a cartridge. It is usually of brass or other metal when used for rifles and handguns. When used for shotguns, it is usually of paper or plastic with a metal head, and is more often called a hull.

cease-fire:

a) As a verb - The command to stop shooting, unload firearms and step behind the cease-fire line.

b) As a noun - Time or period of range inactivity while targets are changed or other activities are conducted.

centre-fire: A cartridge with its primer located in the centre of the base of the case.

chainfiring: The term used to describe the dangerous result of not using grease over the balls used in a black-powder revolver. When the primary cylinder is fired, lack of grease on the other cylinders may cause them to discharge before they are lined up with the barrel.

chamber:

a) The portion at the breech end of the barrel. The cartridge is placed in the chamber ready for firing. A revolver is multi-chambered.

b) To place a cartridge in the barrel.

charge:

a) The amount, by weight, of the powder in a cartridge.

b) In the case of black powder, the amount, by volume, of the powder used.

c) To fill a magazine with cartridges.

Chief Firearms Officer: The person in authority in a province or territory responsible for licences, authorizations to transport, authorizations to carry and other functions related to the administration of the *Firearms Act* and its Regulations.

choke: Narrowing at the muzzle end of a shotgun barrel that determines the shot pattern.

cleaning kit: A set of specialized accessories used to clean and maintain a firearm.

clip: An informal term used to describe a magazine.

cock: To set the action into position for firing. On some firearms, the action has an intermediate position called half cock. On muzzleloading firearms, the cock holds the flint or match.

coking: The burning of black powder residue with much heat and little smoke.

comb: The upper edge of a rifle or shotgun stock where the holder's cheek rests.

conical bullet: A cylindrical-shaped bullet with a cone-shaped tip.

core: The part of a bullet that is covered by a jacket, i.e., the centre of a bullet.

corrosion: The gradual eating away of the metal parts of a firearm caused by rust or other chemical reactions.

crimp: The portion of a cartridge or shell case that is bent inward to hold the bullet or shot in place.

cross-bolt safety: A device that blocks the firing mechanism of a firearm.

cross-hairs: The sighting lines in a telescopic sight.

cylinder: The part of a revolver that rotates and in which chambers are bored to hold cartridges. It combines the functions of magazine, feed system and firing chamber.

cylinder bore: A shotgun barrel having the same diameter throughout, i.e., without choke. It is used to fire solid slugs.

D

dangerous range: The maximum distance at which a projectile will travel. See also **range**.

deactivated firearm: A deactivated firearm is one that has been rendered permanently inoperable. The standards for deactivated firearms are determined by the RCMP/CFP.

direct control: Defined as having the firearm within eyesight and/or arm's reach of the shooter.

dominant eye: See **master eye**.

double action: An action that cocks and fires with a complete pull of the trigger.

double action only: An action that cannot fire in a single action mode.

double-action revolver: A revolver that both cocks and fires with a complete pull of the trigger.

double-barrel: A firearm with two barrels, either side-by-side or one over the other.

down range: The direction from the shooting position towards the target on a range. See also **range**.

dry firing: Firing of an unloaded firearm to practise handling and shooting techniques. This can damage some types of actions, particularly rim-fire.

dummy ammunition: Inactive ammunition used for practising handling of firearms. It has no primers or propellants. See also **live ammunition**.

E

effective range: The maximum distance for a shooter at which he or she can confidently hit the target. Also refers to the useful range of the projectile(s). See also **range**.

ejector: The mechanism that expels the cartridge or case from the firearm.

extraction: The removal of a cartridge or case from the chamber of a firearm.

F

feed: The action of moving a fresh cartridge into the chamber.

feeding path: The path a cartridge follows within an action.

field stripping: Taking apart a firearm for regular maintenance and cleaning.

firearm: See under Appendix C: Legal Definitions.

firing pin: The part of the breech mechanism that strikes the primer of the cartridge.

flash suppressor: Muzzle attachment designed to cool emergent gases and prevent or reduce muzzle flash.

flat-nosed bullet: A bullet with a flattened front end. It is used mainly in cartridges designed for rifles with tubular magazines.

fléchette: A small dart stabilized by fins. It is encased in a discarding sabot (case) and loaded into a shotgun shell. Usually, one shell will contain a number of fléchettes. This type of ammunition is prohibited.

flintlock: The gunlock of early firearms in which flint is struck against steel. This causes sparks to ignite the powder charge.

floor plate: The metal plate at the bottom of some cartridge magazines. (The floor plate is usually hinged at the front and held by a release spring located just ahead of the trigger guard.)

follow-through: Staying in the same position after squeezing the trigger or continuing the swing in firing at a moving target. This helps to shoot accurately.

follower: The part of a magazine between the spring and the ammunition. You must be able to see or feel the follower to know the magazine is empty. See also **magazine follower**.

forcing cone: In smooth bore and revolver barrels, a cone that joins the chamber to the bore. It assists the passage of the projectile(s) into the bore. Also called a throat.

forearm/fore-stock: The forward part of a one or two piece stock. It is sometimes called a slide on pump action firearms.

frizzen: The metal arm of a flintlock mechanism. The flint strikes the frizzen to create sparks in the flash pan. It is also called a battery.

full cock: The position of the hammer or striker when the firearm is ready to fire.

full-metal jacket: A bullet with a jacket, usually of harder metal, encasing the core. It is also called a hard-point bullet. Used in ball ammunition.

G

gauge: The measurement of the diameter of a shotgun bore.

grain: A unit of weight (7,000 grains equal one pound) commonly used to measure the weight of ammunition components. Black powder and its substitutes are measured in grains by volume. Modern powders are measured by weight.

grip: The small portion of the stock gripped by the trigger hand.

grooves: See **rifling**.

H

half cock: A safety feature on some firearms. When the hammer is pulled back half-way, it cannot be fired by squeezing the trigger.

hammer: The part of the action that drives the firing pin forward.

handgun: See under Appendix C: Legal Definitions.

hangfire: A malfunction causing a delay in firing a cartridge after the firing pin has struck the primer.

high power: A term applied to the first smokeless powder cartridges with velocities of approximately 609.6 m/s (2,000 ft./s).

high-powered rifle: Generally, a firearm that uses centre-fire ammunition.

holding: The action of keeping the sights on the target while squeezing the trigger.

hollow point: A bullet with a hollow at the tip (nose) that makes it expand more on impact.

hull: The outer covering or casing of a shotgun shell.

I

No applicable entry.

J

jacket: The outer covering over the inner metal core of a bullet.

K

kick: See **recoil**.

L

lands: See **rifling**.

leading: Particles from shot or bullets that stick to the metal surface of the bore. This is due to heat or friction.

lever action:
a) An action operated by a lever located underneath it. (A secondary purpose of the lever is to serve as a trigger guard.)
b) A repeating firearm that has a magazine and a breech mechanism cycled by an external lever, usually below the receiver or frame.

line of sight: An imaginary straight line from the shooter's eye to the target; usually through the sights.

live ammunition: Ammunition containing primers and propellants capable of firing bullets or other projectiles.

load: To prepare a firearm for firing by inserting ammunition into it.

loading gate: The hinged cover over the opening through which cartridges are inserted into the magazine or chamber.

loading port: The opening through which cartridges are inserted into the magazine or chamber.

lock: The firing mechanism of a muzzleloader. In firearms that are loaded through the breech, the lock is both the firing mechanism and breech-sealing assembly.

long gun: Generic term used to describe rifles and shotguns.

M

magazine: See **cartridge magazine**.

magazine cut off: Disengages magazine feed from firearm.

magazine follower: Spring-loaded platform in a magazine. It pushes cartridges or shells to the feeding position. When checking that a firearm is completely unloaded, the magazine follower should be clearly in view. This is especially important with tubular magazines.

magazine release: A button or switch that allows for the removal of a magazine from the firearm.

magnum:
a) A cartridge or shell with a larger capacity or with a higher velocity than average (e.g., 3.5-inch Magnum shot shell, .300 Winchester Magnum rifle, .44 Remington Magnum handgun). Firearms that use magnum ammunition may also be called magnum.
b) A marketing term used by manufacturers which may or may not indicate greater power or range.

mainspring: A strong spring which activates the striker or hammer of a firearm.

malfunction: The failure of a firearm to work properly. This can be caused by a jam or stoppage, or a mechanical or structural failure.

master eye: The stronger eye; the eye through which a person usually views an object as when sighting a firearm.

match/wick: A long cord soaked in saltpetre, which burns slowly. Used to ignite powder in early firearms.

matchlock: A firearm action that uses a serpentine or S-shaped piece of metal to hold a smouldering match. The burning match contacts the priming powder in the pan to ignite the charge.

metallic cartridge: A cartridge with a metallic case. In contrast, early cartridge cases were made of linen, paper, etc.

mid-range: The point in the trajectory halfway between the muzzle and the target.

Mini-ball or Minie ball: A cylindrical-shaped bullet used in muzzleloaders. It has a pointed tip and a hollow base that spreads as it is fired.

misfire: The failure of a cartridge to fire after the firing pin has struck the primer. Do not confuse with hangfire, which is a delay in firing.

mushroom: The shape many soft-point bullets become when they expand upon impact.

musket: An early smoothbore shoulder firearm.

muzzle: The opening at the end of the barrel from which the bullet or shot emerges.

muzzle brake: A device attached to the muzzle that softens the recoil of the firearm. Also known as a compensator.

muzzleloader: A firearm that is loaded through the muzzle.

N

non-restricted firearm: See under Appendix C: Legal Definitions.

O

open sight: A type of firearm sight, usually with a "V" or "U" notch in the rear sight. See also **sight**.

over-and-under: A firearm, usually a shotgun, with two barrels placed one over the other.

P

pan: The small container located on the side or top of a matchlock, wheel lock or flintlock firearm used to hold the priming powder.

patch:
a) A small piece of leather or cloth that is greased and placed around a bullet before ramming it down the barrel of a muzzleloader.
b) A piece of cloth drawn through the bore of a firearm to clean it.

patch box: A small compartment in the butt of a muzzleloader used to store patches or other small items.

pattern: Distribution of the shot in a shotgun charge. This is measured at a standard distance of 40 yards and in a 30-inch circle.

peep sight: A rear sight with a hole through which the target is viewed. Also known as an aperture sight.

pellet: Small round projectiles loaded into shotgun shells. Usually referred to as shot. Also a lead projectile used in some air guns.

penetration: The depth that a projectile travels into a target before it stops.

percussion cap: A small metal explosive-filled cup that is placed over the nipple of a percussion firearm.

pistol: A small hand-held firearm.

powder: The general term for any propellant used in firearms which burns upon ignition. The two major types are black powder (an explosive) and smokeless powder (a propellant).

powder burn: Charring caused by gunshot residue.

powder charge: The amount of powder by weight in the case of smokeless powder, and by volume, in the case of black powder.

prime: In the case of a black-powder firearm, to place powder on the pan or percussion cap on the nipple. Also, to place a primer in a cartridge case.

primer: The overall term for the priming compound, cup and anvil which, when struck, ignites the powder charge.

primer pop: The sound of only the primer discharging due to no or grossly inadequate charge of powder in the cartridge.

prohibited ammunition: See under Appendix C: Legal Definitions.

prohibited device: See under Appendix C: Legal Definitions.

prohibited firearm: See under Appendix C: Legal Definitions.

projectile: A bullet or shot in flight after firing from a firearm.

propellant: The chemical substance which, when ignited, propels the projectile. Also called powder.

pull-through: The cord used to pull a bore brush or cleaning patch through the bore of a firearm.

pump action:
a) An action that is operated by moving the fore-end in a motion parallel to the bore.
b) A repeating firearm that has a magazine and is manually set in motion usually parallel to the barrel; also called slide action or trombone action.

Q

No applicable entry.

R

ramrod: A wood or metal rod used to push the patch and bullet down the barrel of a muzzleloader.

range:
a) The distance travelled by a projectile from firearm to target.
b) A projectile's maximum travelling distance.
c) An area or facility designed for the safe shooting of firearms.
d) Dangerous range: the maximum distance at which a projectile will travel.
e) Effective range: the greatest distance a projectile will travel with accuracy.

receiver: A firearm's metal frame that generally contains the breech, locking and loading mechanisms. Normally the serial number is on the receiver. Also called the frame.

recoil: The backward movement of a firearm when it is fired. Also called kick.

replica firearm: See under Appendix C: Legal Definitions.

restricted firearm: See under Appendix C: Legal Definitions.

revolver:

a) A repeating handgun that has a revolving cylinder with a series of chambers. The cylinder may revolve in either direction, depending on the manufacturer.

b) A firearm, usually a handgun, that has a revolving cylinder with a series of chambers, and is discharged successively by the same firing mechanism. The chamber may revolve in either direction depending on the manufacturer.

revolving action: An action with a revolving cylinder containing a number of cartridge chambers. One chamber at a time lines up with the barrel.

ricochet: The redirection of a projectile after impact, usually with a hard surface. For example, a bullet bouncing off a rock.

rifle: A shoulder firearm with a rifled bore. Designed to fire one projectile at a time. See also **rifling**.

rifled slug: A large, single projectile with spiral grooves used in shotguns.

rifling: Spiral grooves inside the barrel. Rifling causes the bullet to spin, increasing its accuracy and range. The depressed portions of the rifling are called grooves and the raised portions are called lands.

rim: The edge on the base of a cartridge case. The rim is the part of the case that the extractor grips to remove the cartridge from the chamber.

rim-fire: A cartridge that has its primer located inside the rim of the case. See also **cartridge**.

rod: A rod used for cleaning a firearm. It is used to check for obstructions prior to loading the firearm. It may also be referred to as a ramrod, proving stick or dummy rod.

round: One shot fired by a firearm. It is also a complete item of ammunition or a cartridge that has all the components needed to fire one shot.

round-nose bullet: A bullet with a rounded nose.

S

sabot: A plastic sleeve that holds a slug that is smaller than the bore diameter of a firearm. It is used mainly in shotguns and muzzleloading firearms.

safety: A device that blocks the firing mechanism of a firearm.

scope: See **sight**.

sear: Part of the firing mechanism linked to the trigger. The sear holds the hammer, firing pin or striker in the cocked position until the trigger is squeezed.

secure locking device: See under Appendix C: Legal Definitions.

semi-automatic:
a) An action which fires, extracts, ejects, chambers and cocks with each separate pull of the trigger.
b) A repeating firearm requiring that the trigger be pulled for each shot fired and which uses the energy of the discharge to perform part of the operating cycle; sometimes called auto-loading or self-loading actions.

semi-wadcutter: A cylindrical bullet with a short truncated cone at the nose. Often used for paper target shooting.

shell: A complete unit of ammunition consisting of a hull, primer, powder, wad and projectile(s) for use in shotguns.

shotgun: A shoulder firearm with a smooth bore designed to fire multiple pellets called shot, or a single projectile called a slug.

shot shell / shotgun shell: A cartridge used in a shotgun. It contains multiple shot pellets or a single projectile called a slug.

side by side: A firearm, usually a shotgun, with two barrels placed side by side.

sight: A firearm device, either mechanical or optical, that helps the shooter aim accurately.

single action: An action that releases the hammer from a cocked position when the trigger is pulled. Usually found on handguns.

single action revolver: A revolver that requires the hammer to be cocked manually. Pressing the trigger will not cause it to fire until this is done.

single shot: A single-barrel firearm that is manually loaded and has no magazine-feed device.

slide safety: A device that blocks the firing mechanism of a firearm.

sling: A strap used to carry and aid in aiming a rifle.

slug: A large single projectile used in shotguns. See also **rifled slug**.

small bore: Generally refers to a .22 calibre firearm or rim-fire ammunition.

smokeless powder: Propellant powder used in modern firearms.

smooth bore: A firearm with a bore that is not rifled, such as a shotgun.

soft-point bullet: A bullet with a partial jacket exposing a portion of the lead core at the nose.

spent bullet: A bullet near the end of its flight that has lost nearly all its energy. Despite a loss in energy, spent bullets can still penetrate targets.

spire-point bullet: A bullet with a cone-shaped nose.

stock: The part of a rifle or shotgun used in holding the firearm.

T

tang safety: A device that blocks the firing mechanism of a firearm.

telescopic sight: See **sight**.

trajectory: The path a projectile takes during flight.

trigger: The part of the firearm mechanism that releases the part of the action that fires the cartridge.

trigger guard: The metal loop around the trigger made to protect it and prevent accidentally touching the trigger.

U

unattended: See under <u>Appendix C: Legal Definitions</u>.

unloaded: See under <u>Appendix C: Legal Definitions</u>.

V

vehicle: See under <u>Appendix C: Legal Definitions</u>.

velocity: The speed at which a projectile travels in a given direction.

W

wad: A paper fibre or plastic disc used to separate the powder charge from the shot or slug, to seal propellant gases behind the charge, and to hold the shot together in the barrel.

wad-cutter: A cylindrical bullet with a sharp, shouldered, nearly flat nose. It is designed to cut paper targets cleanly so they can be scored accurately.

wheel lock: An early firearm mechanism. A wheel with serrated edges is spun against a piece of iron pyrite. This sends sparks into the pan to ignite the charge.

wing safety: A device that blocks the firing mechanism of a firearm.

X

No applicable entry.

Y

No applicable entry.

Z

No applicable entry.

All instructors who teach the Canadian Firearms Safety Course (CFSC) and the Canadian Restricted Firearms Safety Course (CRFSC) must meet and maintain certain service standards and quality of instruction. The Canadian Firearms Program (CFP) relies on student feedback in order to monitor and constantly improve how this firearms safety training is being provided.

If you would like to provide feedback to the CFP regarding your CFSC or CRFSC training experience, we welcome you to contact us at: CFO_Program-Programme_CAF@rcmp-grc.gc.ca